HEAT AND I

A PRACTICAL GUIDE TO ENERGY CONSERVATION IN CHURCH BUILDINGS

Brian Marks

with chapters by

Ian G Hanna

SAINT ANDREW PRESS

EDINBURGH

First published in 1994 by
SAINT ANDREW PRESS

on behalf of
The GENERAL TRUSTEES
of the CHURCH OF SCOTLAND
121 George Street, Edinburgh EH2 4YN.

ISBN 0 86153 169 8

British Library Cataloguing in Publication Data
A catalogue record for this book
is available from the British Library.

ISBN 086153169 8

Typeset in Garamond.
Printed and bound by Bell and Bain Ltd, Glasgow.

CONTENTS

FOREWORD

Few church members may be aware of the remarkable service which has been offered to congregations over many years by the Church of Scotland's Energy Consultant Brian Marks and his lighting counterpart Ian Hanna. But many church members have felt and seen the results of their endeavours and many church treasurers have reason to be grateful for the sound practical advice offered by these two invaluable servants of the Church.

It is both the policy and a fundamental conviction of the Christian Church that wise stewardship must be exercised over all resources. The cause of energy conservation in the Church of Scotland, and beyond, was originally championed by the Kirk's 'Society, Religion and Technology Project' and quickly taken up by the General Trustees and the Board of Stewardship and Finance. In this area at least the Church moved actively to practise what it preached!

Under the auspices of the Society, Religion and Technology Project of the Church of Scotland previous titles by Brian Marks have appeared, *'Make the Most of It!'* (SRT 1980) and *Make Even More of It* (SRT 1986), and these books have found a place in church bookshelves across the globe.

The present work goes beyond these publications in seeking to provide a comprehensive introductory guide to all aspects of energy use in church buildings. Conservation is seen as a natural part of overall stewardship and management within the context of congregational life.

In presenting this publication for the attention of all those concerned with the well-being of the people as well as the buildings of the Church, the General Trustees would wish to pay warm tribute to the authors Brian Marks and Ian Hanna, and to express their thanks to the Board of Stewardship and Finance for their assistance with the publication of this volume, the Society, Religion and Technology Project for their inspiration and encouragement, and to Dr Donald Smith, Secretary of the Advisory Committee on Artistic Matters, who co-ordinated preparation of the final text.

Robin Martin
CHAIRMAN
The Church of Scotland General Trustees

INTRODUCTION

This book is intended as a practical guide for the church office-bearer. For this reason it is by no means technical, and where calculations can be helpful these are kept as simple as possible and are hopefully within the grasp of most who are likely to be saddled with responsibility in this field.

Apart from giving guidance on types of heating and lighting and comparative effectiveness and efficiency, the book should enable the reader to make basic checks on energy use in any set of church buildings.

It is not intended to take the place of the consultant nor to make the reader a competent heating engineer, but it will give help at all stages of discussion and assessment of proposals for upgrading or replacement. Some advice on finding experts and working with them is included.

Congregations tend to take a serious look at heating only when the heating system has been giving operational problems, or has become recognized as giving sub-standard comfort relative to current expectations, or they have become conscious of the size of their energy bills usually through the arrival of some unexpectedly big ones. Lighting is subject to even less frequent consideration.

This is reasonable enough because heating and lighting are things that should go along quietly without distracting attention from the main objects of the church. However, poor heating in particular can have quite drastic effects on church attendance. Large bills can divert hard-won money from more worthy projects.

The chapters relating to heating and energy are based on experience accumulated in over 1000 surveys of churches with and without associated hall accommodation. Almost every practical form of heating has been checked over time after time in relation to all sorts and conditions of buildings.

There is a limitation. While buildings belonging to most denominations have been surveyed, by far the largest number have been Church of Scotland buildings located in Scotland. To this extent the churches have generally been heated only on Sundays apart from additional heatings for special services including weddings and funerals. The halls have had widely varying intensity of use. Figures for energy use suggested as targets are based on experience of average Scottish conditions and need adjustment for significantly different climatic conditions.

Lighting is a relatively small item in terms of total energy use, but because of the structure of some tariffs it can represent quite a high proportion of expenditure on energy. Mr Ian Hanna has wide experience in this field and has contributed two chapters on the subject.

When the Church of Scotland Energy Survey scheme was launched in 1979 the main object was to try to help avoid waste of God-given limited natural resources and congregational offerings. At that time pollution was not an important issue.

It is now realised that CO_2 is a very serious by-product of energy use. We are faced with the awesome consequences of global warming and enormous difficulties in trying to get a co-ordinated worldwide approach to the problem.

This can lead to a feeling of helplessness and a tendency to dismiss it as being something completely outside the control of the individual or congregation.

However this is a world problem where there is no conflict between self-interest and that of mankind as a whole. It also gives congregations an opportunity to take a lead and set an example to the community at large.

Avoid waste of energy and this in turn saves money, saves diminishing resources, reduces pollution and reduces global warming.

The only problem – and it is not an easy one – is how far to go along the energy saving trail in any specific instance. At the limit you could fully insulate a building at huge cost and build wind-generators nearby to provide most of the energy requirements, but the costs would be impossible to contemplate.

Looked at another way, you could simply not heat the buildings and depend on people coming clad to withstand the worst. This is equally impracticable.

In terms of practical energy conservation the first action should always be to make the best of what you have and not scrap good equipment in chasing after the ultimate in efficiency. Changes in global energy use can only be gradual and church congregations are rarely in the position where they can afford to be the adventurous leaders in new technology – quite the reverse. What is essential in heating church buildings with limited, changing and increasingly voluntary supervision is reliability and simplicity.

This book does not have a chapter on energy conservation as such, but at the same time it is all about *practical* energy conservation: how to start from where you are and look at people and buildings and heating and lighting and the bits and pieces of equipment so that you have a better chance of taking the right decisions to give the users of your buildings acceptable conditions with the practical minimum of waste, and without getting the congregation into unnecessary debt to achieve it.

ACKNOWLEDGMENTS

The Society Religion and Technology Project of the Church of Scotland has published two books on energy use in church buildings. *Make the Most of It* was published in 1980 and *Make Even More of It* in 1986 as a supplement and update. This book supersedes these, and permission to use some material which originally appeared in them is gratefully acknowledged.

Thanks are due to Russell McLarty and Jim McQueen who read and commented on the original manuscript of Chapters 1 to 12. Their comments, based on extensive experience, have been most helpful and have contributed significantly to the final version. Any shortcomings remain the responsibility of the author!

(1)
PEOPLE

Keeping people comfortable is the prime object of heating church buildings, but this is not just a matter of getting the air temperature up to a specified figure and leaving it at that.

The body is sensitive to air temperature and radiant temperature (from the fabric or elsewhere) and can be comfortable within a range of combinations of the two figures. The body is also sensitive to air movement and becomes more sensitive to this if the moving air is cooler than the main body of air, *ie* a draught! (There is more on this subject in the section headed *People Heating* at the end of this chapter.)

People wear different clothes. It is interesting that ladies tend to keep coats on in church while men remove them. Men's legs tend to be better insulated than ladies, unless the ladies are wearing long boots when the situation is probably reversed, unless long-johns are concealed below the men's trousers.

But this is only the starting point on the interaction between people and heating. In practice it has been found that heating and energy saving problems are almost equally divided between truly technical matters and those with a substantial 'people factor'.

In any given situation someone will be responsible for the day-to-day operation of heating. This will often be a church officer or hall keeper. This person is right in the front line if anything goes wrong and very naturally tries to do his or her very best to ensure that complaints are kept to a minimum. (There is of course always someone who can never be satisfied!)

Now this is fine, except that under this pressure the person in charge has to err on the side of being generous with settings just to avoid trouble. This is a much greater pressure than that of the treasurer or the

4

management committee who usually only get round to thinking about costs once a year when the 'Heat and Light' figure appears on the annual accounts.

There are exceptions because there are people looking after heating systems who really take economy to heart and heat the buildings for such short times at such low temperatures that no one could ever be comfortable. This is done with the best of intentions but can end up with reducing congregations, especially when older people find that the situation is unbearable. Instead of the intended economy this is a very wasteful approach, because there is often little difference in cost between heating to a point that is just short of comfort level and actually making the church or hall comfortable. Most of the cost is incurred in getting up to the nearly-comfortable situation and a fraction more can make all the difference.

Such actions by a dedicated church officer or volunteer are more often the cause of poor heating than is generally recognized. Because the action is well meant, if mistaken, the correction of this particular problem can involve delicate negotiations and has been known to lead to a great deal of emotional stress. An independent report can be very useful.

PEOPLE AND THERMOSTATS

People love to play with thermostats. If a thermostat is set at anything less than maximum some people have an overpowering desire to turn it right up. When that happens you might as well not have one at all. At home, thermostats are usually treated with more respect because there is a recognition that there is some sort of connection between temperature and bills. However, that does not seem to appear to be the case when they are in the church or hall.

Even when the dials are concealed there are those who will unscrew the covers just to turn the setting up. Some have been encased in boxes with padlocked doors to prevent this. Unless the box is carefully designed this can have the opposite to the desired effect because it makes the thermostat less responsive.

There are those who advocate the installation of two thermostats. One with a concealed face is set to control the heating at the level required and the other has an exposed face but is not connected to anything. It is provided for the fiddlers!

There is just an element of justification in turning up the thermostat to maximum if starting from cold, or if the room feels cold when you come into it – and this is tied up with the body's response to radiant and air temperature. When the walls and the rest of the fabric are cold you need a higher air temperature to feel comfortable. As the temperature of the fabric increases you feel comfortable at a lower air temperature. The trouble is that people who turn up thermostats usually forget to turn them down again. (Thermostats are more fully discussed in chapters 8 and 9).

THE KEY PEOPLE – INCLUDING THE ENERGY OFFICER

If there is a moral to be drawn from all of this, it is that in looking after heating and energy two heads are definitely better than one. A church officer or hall keeper has a lot of other duties besides looking after the heating, and though in many cases now they are volunteers from among the office-bearers they are just as likely to be employed by the congregation and have no voice at meetings.

This is only one of the reasons why it is really useful to have an energy officer on the appropriate committee. Many congregations have separate finance and property committees. The energy officer's duties are difficult to categorise in this way and there is a good case for reporting to the main management committee. This will usually only take a few minutes at a meeting but has the merit of keeping energy use on the agenda. In most cases the costs involved will be among the largest over which the congregation has direct control.

This person should have responsibility for keeping an eye on overall energy use by setting targets and then monitoring by maintaining records of consumption. Regular monthly readings are more useful than weekly readings which tend to produce a clutter of figures that are demanding to collect and difficult to analyse. (Weekly and even daily or half-daily readings have their place in searching for causes of high consumption, but not as a routine.)

Other duties should include consideration of the relative points made in this book and of course giving advice and support to the church officer or other person in the firing line. The starting point has to be with Chapter 12 – Targeting and Monitoring.

PEOPLE HEATING

People are self-heating and each person puts out surplus heat. Typically the figure will be about 100 watts, but this can rise by nearly half as much again with a good-going hymn. (It drops quite a lot when sleeping!)

In practical terms this means that a congregation of 300 in an average-sized church will add about half the heat output of the heating system. This will suggest one way of keeping costs down. (It helps, too, if people can be encouraged to sit together – at least for those on the inside.)

As far as the individual is concerned they are generally losing heat to the surroundings and the object of heating is to counteract this. The extent and nature of clothing has an important influence but broadly the body will be roughly equally sensitive to air temperature and 'radiant' temperature (with a bias towards the latter). The former is readily understood and is measured by thermometers and conventional thermo-stats. A special type of 'globe' thermometer is needed to measure radiant temperature.

In practical terms this means that a person will be reasonably comfortable in a range of roughly 12°C radiant/20°C air to 20°C radiant/12°C air. A cold wall will affect you whether you are near it or in the middle of the building. This is important because it explains some things which can be puzzling unless this basic fact is appreciated.

Air movement (otherwise, a draught) also influences comfort.

In the old days a coal-fired boiler was started on Friday night and ran through to Sunday morning. The heating installation was undersized by present standards but the long period of soaking meant that the whole fabric was well heated. On a Sunday morning the air temperature may have been no more than the high 50s (°F) (say 13/14°C) but because the radiant temperature was more or less the same and people were wearing more clothes, they were comfortable.

Then came the change to oil with increasing costs and preheat periods were shortened so that the fabric was not so well heated. Higher air temperatures were needed to compensate and often the boiler or heating installation did not have the capacity to cope with this. This was compensated for initially by the fact that people still wore relatively heavy clothing, but fashions and materials have changed.

There is of course another way of raising the radiant temperature and this is to use radiant heaters of any type. Ideally these are located to compensate for the cold fabric and this is why they are particularly effective if they heat the part of the body that is exposed to the walls. A striking example of this is the use of low temperature panel heaters in pews where, with a short preheat period, you can sit in comfort in the pews, but as soon as you stand up you are aware of the upper part of your body being surrounded by cold air. This makes for very economical heating though most people would opt for a little more heat to take the chill off the air and make the building feel more welcoming.

This same characteristic explains why you cannot depend on the calibrations of an air thermostat in a church particularly, but also in intermittently heated halls. It is better to set the thermostat by experience to control at a comfortable level. The setting will vary according to fabric temperature and this is why it is helpful to turn the thermostat down a few degrees at the beginning and end of the season, or during an unseasonable mild spell, to prevent the building becoming oppressively hot.

CASE NOTES

Office-bearers believed that the minister was 'messing-around' with the heating and took steps to prevent him from gaining access to the boilerhouse by changing locks. They promptly put up their costs by

£1000 a year. Investigation revealed that all the minister had really been doing was helping the lady church officer by opening and closing the valve serving the church heating which she could not reach. The change coincided with a change to a male church officer who, like everyone else apart from the minister, did not know about the valve. The net result was that the church was heated whenever the halls were in use.

A minister, who was near retiring age, asked the consultant to consider recommending a time switch to control the heating in the church. He was quite happy to continue his practice of getting up at four or five on a Sunday morning, getting dressed and walking 100 yards to the church to switch on the heating, but felt that it would be only fair to his successor to have a less arduous arrangement.

Another minister near retirement had a church with a hot water system but no piped water supply. There was a small leak in the system below the pulpit that was considered to be too expensive to repair. Every Saturday evening the minister filled a two-gallon container at the manse, took it by car to the church, climbed on to a table in the vestry and topped up the header tank. Then he switched on the boiler. The saddest part was that his congregation included some very wealthy individuals.

A modest church had a very popular and well-known minister. The church had many strangers who came to fill the church at every service. The heating system was theoretically inadequate but there were no complaints and energy use was low. The minister passed on. The new young minister had the support of his congregation but the visitors disappeared and it was only then that they discovered that they had a heating problem.

(2)

BUILDINGS

The buildings and their pattern of use are the starting point on any study of energy use or heating.

Church buildings can vary enormously in size, type, construction *etc*. A church may stand alone or have halls attached. In every case there are heat losses and most of the heat put into buildings is to compensate for this. In each case it is necessary to identify the main loss areas and consider whether any action is necessary *and* practicable.

Heat is dissipated into the fabric and in air escaping from the building. Losses to the fabric can be lessened by increasing the insulation value of the fabric surfaces. Losses in the air are lowered by reducing the rate of movement of the air through and out of the building.

Practicality is emphasised because in churches (as distinct from halls) it is usually quite impracticable to try to prevent losses to the fabric by improving insulation. On the other hand there are often opportunities to reduce losses caused by air infiltration into and out of the building.

WARNING – CONDENSATION

In determining the practicality of any specific action which will alter the characteristics of heat and air movement, it is important to take into account the possible effects on the fabric of the building. Major changes in the heating system can also have side effects.

It is all too easy to innocently create a situation where there is insufficient air movement to remove water vapour and this can lead very quickly to the development of rot. There is also the danger of ending up with condensation in an undesirable and 'out of sight – out of mind' location with similar consequences.

It is not possible to deal with these matters in a general fashion as each situation will be different. Contractors' advice can be helpful up to a point, but if an architect is not involved in the design, the safest approach is to engage either a building surveyor or an architect with experience of church buildings to confirm that any substantial changes to insulation or ventilation will not harm the fabric.

Some congregations are tempted to go overboard on insulation and draughtproofing if only to demonstrate their enthusiasm for stewardship and to try to make certain they are wasting the absolute minimum of energy. The intention is commendable but it is important to bear the above points in mind.

INSULATION OF CHURCHES

Because of the strong emphasis on the benefits of the insulation of houses there is a widespread belief that insulation can be of considerable help in the church situation.

This is not the case, especially in churches used primarily for Sunday services when the periods at full heat are very short. The following is an over-simplification but will illustrate the point.

There are two factors to be taken into account in calculating the savings from insulation. One is the temperature difference from inside to out, and the other is time. Though it may take some hours to heat a church, the initial temperature is usually not that much above the outside temperature and then increases progressively to comfort level which should be reached just shortly before the service and is held for the duration. Thus the full theoretical saving can usually only be achieved for two to four hours a week. For the rest of the time the heating is on, the saving will average out at about half the theoretical figure. The result is a situation where the cost of adding insulation is generally completely out of scale with potential savings.

Even if the roof is suited to loft insulation the saving tends to be very small, because with a typical lath and plaster ceiling its temperature has to be raised significantly before there is any reduction in heat flow due to insulation applied above it.

Suspended ceilings and timber ceilings are cases where insulation will make a more significant, but still modest, saving provided that they can support the additional weight.

In the case of lofts the addition of insulation will always reduce the access of circulating air to the ceiling timbers with some attendant, if small, risk. There is no point in taking this risk if there is no real benefit to be gained.

From the point of view of energy saving, the correct place to install insulation in a church is on the internal surfaces so that heat does not get into the fabric in the first place. This is expensive and in most cases would give an unacceptable change in the appearance of the building, quite apart from any potential side effects on the fabric.

Commercial double-glazing is not a very good energy saving investment in a house, taking typically 20 plus years to recover the cost out of savings. It is even worse in the typical church where it could take as much as 100 years based on savings due solely to improved insulation properties.

If the church is heated on a daily basis then the following comments on halls will be more appropriate.

INSULATION OF HALLS

It is much more likely that some savings can be made by applying insulation in halls — because they are heated for longer periods. As a rule of thumb, if the building is fully heated and occupied for more than about 20 hours a week it is worth considering low cost loft insulation at least.

The best material is glass fibre or equivalent mats to at least 100mm. The suitability of the ceiling must be taken into account. Many church hall ceilings are level centrally and follow the line of the roof towards the walls. The sloping sides should not be insulated as it is very easy to block ventilation if insulation is pushed blindly into these areas. Vapour barriers should be installed as appropriate and expert advice should be taken.

As far as double-glazing is concerned, the hall that is used morning, afternoon and evening during the week will be similar to a house with a payback period on commercial windows of 20 plus years.

Despite the earlier comments on double-glazing, if you have a situation where it is necessary to replace the windows in any case (*eg* because of rotting frames) the additional cost of double-glazing will probably not be all that much and will generally be justified if there is a minimum heated use of at least 20 hours a week.

If walls are brick with a cavity there could be a case for insulating. In practice many brick built halls have relatively little exposed outer wall which is both suitable for insulating and is also exposed to full temperature. Advice, preferably from an architect or building surveyor, should be obtained in every case where this is being considered. Care should be taken in selecting a contractor, both as to reputation and nature of guarantees offered − especially as to their validity if the contractor goes out of business. Dry-fill material is generally less likely to give problems.

The application of internal or external surface insulation will generally not be appropriate because of cost and appearance.

A possible exception is the flat-roofed hall. These were often constructed with no insulation, or very little, and with no practical means of adding it except at high cost. Such roofs often have an outer covering which has to be periodically renewed. Depending on the detail of the roof construction it may be practicable to incorporate a layer of insulation in the new covering and this should be raised with the architect concerned or advice sought from a building surveyor.

There is of course heat loss through the floor. It is fairly difficult to add insulation on the underside of the floor and usually the cost would not be justified. In some very exposed sites it can be useful to restrict the airflow under the church by closing some underfloor ventilators. However this should only be done with care and preferably with professional advice and certainly all ventilators should be reopened as soon as the coldest conditions have passed.

A new building or an extension will, of course, incorporate insulation to comply with current standards.

AIR INFILTRATION

In a heated building the buoyancy of the heated air tends to induce a chimney effect drawing air in at low level and expelling it at high level.

There are cases where open doors and windows and gaps in the fabric plus a wind will lead additionally to a sweep through at low level.

If a church has controllable ventilation there can be a distinction between the degree provided during heating (and heated occupation) and that provided at other times. In the first case minimum and possibly zero formal ventilation is often adequate (particularly if the congregation is small relative to the size of the building) while for the rest of the time good ventilation is necessary for the fabric.

Ventilators

Ventilation is something that has been treated differently in churches depending on when they were built, and ranges from nothing at all in the way of specific ventilators to huge openings provided in the days of gas lighting and possibly flueless direct gas heating.

Where there are controls on roof ventilators it is particularly valuable to have them opened as soon as the service finishes so that the combination of open ventilators, open doors and warm buoyant air will lead to rapid and effective removal of moisture. Many have fallen into disuse but are capable of restoration.

Wall ventilators are usually accessible and should be opened and closed as with roof ventilators.

With fixed ventilators, especially in Victorian churches, it is usually feasible to reduce the total, but the minimum necessary for the building and the comfort of occupants must be retained.

If there is mechanical air extraction it is useful to have this stopped after a few hours preferably by timer or time switch — and certainly before the start of the next heating period.

Where the ventilation of the roof space is altered it is important to inspect the space frequently during the first year or two so that corrective action can be taken quickly should the change lead to condensation or other undesirable consequence. Similarly, a watch should also be kept for any tell-tale signals in the interior of the building. This vigilance is important even where professional advice has been taken.

NOTE: There are cases, usually near the west coast and on the islands, where, because of a combination of high humidity and little or no facility for ventilation, condensation can be a problem which is not readily solved. Under such conditions a dehumidifier may provide the most satisfactory solution. These units are inexpensive to buy and run and will make the building easier to heat. To operate effectively, ventilation should be reduced to a minimum and the controls on the unit should be set to maintain a relative humidity in the bracket of 70 to 80. To aim for lower figures could lead to problems with drying out. This note is for general guidance only and further advice should be taken in any specific case – see WARNING – CONDENSATION at the beginning of this chapter.

Windows

Whilst there is rarely a good case for applying double-glazing to improve insulation, there is sometimes a marginally better case for an outer sheet of glazing on leaded windows. Such secondary glazing can reduce air infiltration and also protect the leading from further deterioration. In assessing the value of such treatment it is advisable to regard the protection as the main justification rather than energy savings, unless the leakage is exceptionally bad. The effect on the appearance of the windows must also be taken into account.

The addition of internal glazing will reduce air ingress but may well lead to more rapid deterioration of leading due to isolation of the window from heating.

Opening windows or opening sections should be checked for fit and repaired or given draughtproofing treatment as necessary.

Draughts experienced near windows are generally caused not by air coming through the windows but by air circulation within the building. Warm air rises in the body of the building and comes in contact with the windows where it is cooled and falls down the face of the window to the sill which deflects it back in. This is particularly true where there is no heating at the foot of a window.

Where there is a serious problem it may not be too difficult to add some local electric heating used only for the period of occupation.

Another useful device is a low inner 'window' fitted more or less flush with the inner face of the window recess and up to about a metre high, sealed to the wall all round except for the top. This device traps the falling cold air and tends to raise the level of any cross-flow above the heads of the occupants.

Bearing in mind that in halls a high proportion of the time when heating is on is after dark, good heavy curtains can be almost as effective as double glazing. A lower cost solution is to install simple hinged shutters which can be made of plywood.

Doors

These should be draughtproofed within practical limits. It must be emphasised that any treatment which makes a door hard to shut could increase rather than reduce losses. Draughtproofing is much more cost effective than curtains which often do no more than deflect the draught.

Automatic door closers are every bit as important. There are cases where it may be felt to be impracticable, but the provision of an easily operated door catch to hold the door open when absolutely necessary will usually satisfy the need. Some door closers can be quite expensive but there are simple relatively low cost spring units which can be applied to many doors.

The use of small 'air curtain' heaters over doors does not prevent the ingress of air through the doorway when it is open. They give a sensation of warmth as you pass under them and air is locally warmed, but a check will show that in most cases cold draughts continue below waist level. The really powerful units used in some stores are quite different in design and would be of prohibitive cost. In a church vestibule it is generally a waste of money to put them over the outside doors where most of the warm air is lost outside. They are more useful if located over the outside of inner doors. It is important to make certain that such heaters are not left on accidentally when office-bearers go into church – or worse still when everyone goes home. A timer which will restrict operation to a maximum of about half an hour will prevent this.

AIR MOVEMENT WITHIN THE CHURCH

However effective the draughtproofing is, it will often be found that draughts remain and may in some cases change in the course of a service. These are generated mainly by the heating system and in some cases also by heat given off by the congregation. Heat generated draughts are at their worst when the building is being warmed up and can sometimes be reduced by extending the length of the preheat period to allow more stable conditions to be established before occupation.

It is all a matter of relative air and fabric temperatures. Warm air rises, is then cooled in contact with cold surfaces and falls. When it reaches the floor it is drawn across to the source of the original updraught which will normally be a heater, but may in certain circumstances be the congregation.

Draughts in a church can be very difficult to deal with, but there are some basic pointers which can be given for guidance.

One of the most common locations for draughts is near a pipe organ. The organ often gets the blame and in some cases where the organ blower takes in cold air from below the floor or outside, it certainly will make a contribution. The main cause is the organ loft which is normally unheated. In this situation warm air will find its way into the chamber at high level, be cooled and find its way out again at low level — usually to the discomfort of the choir.

There is no general answer to this, apart from suggesting that if it is not too bad it should be accepted. The ideal answer from the engineer's point of view would be to put heating in the organ chamber, but at the extent needed to be fully effective this is a guaranteed method of destroying an organ! In some cases it may be possible to baffle the air flow at low level and direct it above head level without upsetting the sound. It may be practicable to add some heating between the organ chamber and the occupied seats. Whatever idea is considered it is essential that it is discussed with your organ tuner or builder *before* doing anything.

Where a pipe organ has been removed or fallen into disuse most of the options mentioned will be possible. Some air circulation should be retained for the sake of the fabric.

There are many cases where the raised dais in the pulpit/communion table area has been extended and in doing so radiators have been removed or pipes covered or boxed in. Any such action will upset the balance of the system, leading to a down-draught which sweeps out into the choir or congregation at low level. Compensation must be made for any heating removed.

Where there are galleries and full length windows there are usually gaps between the glass and the gallery. These gaps are sometimes open but more often are either permanently closed or fitted with a hinged flap. If there is no heating in the gallery and the gaps are closed, there will be a tendency to have a stuffy area under the gallery and, possibly, cold draughts, rather like a waterfall, immediately in front of the gallery. This problem can often be reduced by opening at least some of the gaps and allowing warm air to rise up through them back to the gallery. It is a matter for experiment.

If there is heating in the gallery there will probably be no benefit in opening the gaps unless the under-gallery area is stuffy.

Considerable care has to be exercised when separating the area under a gallery from the church proper to form a hall or rooms. If there is no heating in the gallery this can lead to down-draughts in the pews immediately in front of it. This is caused by the loss of the screen of warm air rising from the heating under the gallery through window gaps and up the front. Some heating should be added at the back of the gallery and also at ground floor level below the gallery front.

A very similar situation can also arise when the back of an ungalleried church is isolated to form a hall or rooms leaving a space above which remains part of the church's heated volume. The most satisfactory solution in this case is to carry the division up to the roof (with provision for ventilation of the isolated area). Alternatively heaters should be installed as described above.

HEATED VOLUME

A source of economy and possibly increased comfort can be the reduction of the heated volume. In some cases this may be a matter of a change

HOW A POPULAR CONVERSION CAN CAUSE DRAUGHTS

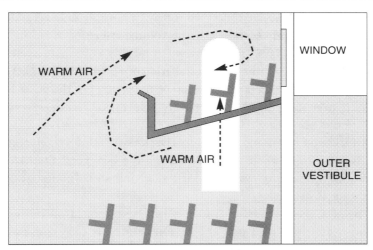

WINDOW

WARM AIR

WARM AIR

OUTER VESTIBULE

Before conversion – no heating in gallery, but warm air circulating

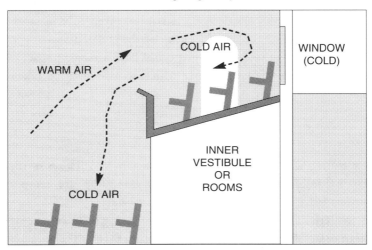

COLD AIR

WINDOW (COLD)

WARM AIR

INNER VESTIBULE OR ROOMS

COLD AIR

After conversion – cold air spills out of gallery onto
new back pews
Action – Add heat under back gallery window and
under new back pew

in design or control of the heating system to avoid heating areas which are unoccupied.

As far as buildings are concerned it may be possible to lower ceilings. This is normally only economic if the volume reduction is substantial. In round terms a 10% reduction will probably cost more than it is worth. An example of this is the installation of a ceiling halfway between the apex of a sloping roof and the top of the walls. On the other hand, anything over about 25% will probably give a good return especially if insulation is also installed.

A reduction in volume will reduce the size of heating system required and there are cases where a lowered ceiling can be a good alternative to upgrading the heating system as well as giving an on-going reduction in heating costs.

The area above or below a gallery can be curtained off during the heating season provided that the heating system is such that the area curtained off can also have the heat input reduced. This can be carried a stage further by permanently separating an unused area. When carrying out any such changes consideration has to be given to ventilation and the provision of some restricted heating of the isolated area.

Changes such as those mentioned could have a major impact on the internal appearance of the building which will have to be taken into account.

CASE NOTES

A new church was constructed with insufficient ventilation in the roof space. A combination of condensation and appropriate temperature conditions led to dry rot within a couple of years.

A modern church hall had large extract fans which were controlled by thermostat. As soon as the air temperature rose to the set point the fans came on and removed most of the heated air. Running costs were about four times what would normally be expected.

A country church with space to spare was split into two sections preserving one end as the church and converting the other into a hall. Only the appropriate part was heated as required.

(3)
HEATING – INTRODUCTION

This subject is dealt with fully in the following chapters but there are some generally applicable points which are better made before proceeding to detail.

A frequent query is 'What is the best heating system for a church (or hall)?'.

The general answer is 'What have you got?'. This may not seem very helpful but it is practical, because even if there are quite serious problems with heating it is unusual to find that the best overall solution is complete replacement.

There are, of course, exceptions such as occurred all over the country in the extreme frosts of the winter of 1981/2 when complete hot water systems were reduced to heaps of scrap. There are cases where a decision to remove pews or otherwise modify buildings may make change essential.

Some 'dry' and very efficient heating systems have to be virtually completely replaced every 20 to 25 years.

Apart from such cases and instances where cast-iron installations have developed recurring leaks, very few systems are likely to need complete replacement, though many could benefit greatly from a degree of upgrading or partial replacement.

For comparison, take a typical church with a volume of about 3000m³ used primarily on Sundays, but with about a dozen extra heated services during the year. At 1993 prices the difference in running cost between the most efficient heating system and an old but adequate (possibly upgraded) cast-iron hot water heating system powered by an efficient standard gas boiler is likely to be no more than £300 per annum. To install a completely new system could be expected to cost from £12,000 to £20,000 depending on type, *ie* a payback period of from 40 to 60 years. The lower end of the capital scale is represented by 'dry' systems, some of which have the short working life referred to above.

More energy is used in halls and thus there is more potential for saving.

If a new system is genuinely needed, the answer to the original question must be conditioned by such factors as the type of building, the pattern and purpose of use, the availability of alternative energy sources, degree of comfort required and availability of capital.

So there is no ready answer to the question. The following chapters discuss the main systems and methods of control. Chapter 10 gives more general guidance on how to go about dealing with the problem as a whole.

For convenience of reference, Hot Water Central Heating has been covered in two separate chapters: the first (Chapter 4) deals with Heat Emitters *ie* radiators, convectors and so on, while Chapter 5 deals with Boilers.

Chapters 6 and 7 are devoted to direct heating, *ie* heating other than by hot water.

Controls are separated into Chapter 8 dealing with the subject generally and, because of their greater complexity, Chapter 9 dealing with central heating controls.

ADVICE

Do remember that most people in the business with whom you discuss the subject have an axe to grind — however much they may try to give you a balanced view. You would not expect a gas company to advocate an electrical solution any more than the other way round. Independent contractors of all sorts will have their specialities. (Above all, almost everyone will try to persuade you to install a complete new system — supplied by themselves.)

It is hoped that the following chapters will give sufficient information to highlight differences and limitations so that it will be possible to have discussions, ask the right questions, and know where to probe further.

The best approach in the long run is to take the advice of an independent consultant with specialist experience of heating and energy saving in churches and church halls. True independence is important if you are to avoid biased sales pressure. In general, the best method of locating such a person will be through the local or central organisations of your own or other Church.

SAFETY AND EFFICIENCY
THROUGH CHECKING AND SERVICING

Checking and servicing will be referred to in various contexts. It is essential that there should be at least an annual inspection and operational check of *all* components of every heating system to maintain safety and performance.

In the case of electrical installations, annual testing and certification by a competent approved contractor is obligatory. This is a matter of safety. This check will not cover the detailed operation of thermostatic and time controls which are important for efficiency.

Most, but by no means all, boilers are regularly serviced and perhaps checked also by an engineer for insurance purposes, but pumps, thermostats, fans and especially sophisticated controls are often completely neglected.

All direct gas heaters, including fires and convectors, and their controls need attention both for safety and performance.

HOT WATER CENTRAL HEATING – HEAT EMITTERS

Heat emitters are the parts of the central heating system that transfer heat from the hot water to the building and its contents.

OLD SYSTEMS – CAST-IRON PIPES AND RADIATORS

Pipes were the original heat emitters especially in churches where large bore pipes were installed around the walls, sometimes up the middle of the church and frequently in ducts which usually corresponded to the aisles. Smaller pipes have been used extensively under fixed pews.

With the exception of the ducted pipes, which will be discussed further below, this is essentially a very good and useful form of heat emitter. It is true that these pipes contain more metal and the large 4″ bore pipes especially hold more water than the pipes used in modern systems, but they perform a dual function of distributing heat and emitting it. For example, a pair of 4″ pipes emit about 0.6kW per meter run. Located round the walls in particular they put heat exactly where it is needed. The central pair of pipes which are often found help to counteract down-draughts as do underpew pipes.

Modern installations are more efficient because less metal and water has to be brought up to working temperature each time the system is switched on, but the saving from a complete change in a typical church may be no more than a hundred or so pounds a year at a capital cost of many thousands. Furthermore the cast iron pipes may very well have more life left in them than the total life of replacement steel emitters.

Cast-iron radiators again contain more metal and water than modern equivalents and therefore there is a slight loss in overall efficiency, but they are not less effective and are very much more durable than the modern counterpart.

There is not therefore a clear case for replacement of old cast-iron systems especially in intermittently heated churches.

As a general rule a cast-iron system should be judged on its condition. If there have been no leaks, or only an isolated case at joints, then there is probably no good case for replacement. If on the other hand there have been recurring leaks, then it is probably better to scrap the pipes even if radiators are retained.

It is often said that the old pipes are 'silted up' or 'full of corrosion'. Silting can be flushed out with water. Under some conditions a mild treatment with appropriate proprietary chemicals can help. Restriction of pipes with a build-up of solid material or serious thinning with corrosion are not all that common unless there has been prolonged leakage and certainly should not be assumed without first cutting out a section for proper investigation. If there is poor circulation the problem is much more likely to lie with a pump or perhaps a pump bypass valve left open. The cost of investigation will be very much less than the cost of a complete replacement system.

Having said this, ducted hot water pipes are a rather special category. A lot of heat is lost to the ducts and the circulation of air around them is generally not very good, which in turn makes them very much less efficient than either above floor pipes or modern systems. When they are closely packed into a duct they can be very difficult to repair because of problems of access. Floor grilles are often a nuisance. There is a good case for replacing these with alternative emitters above floor level at the first sign of trouble. It is not always necessary to remove them provided that a means can be found to isolate them.

Another area where there is higher than average probability of serious deterioration is in buried distribution pipes, possibly leading from the boiler house. It may be possible to replace these without changing the actual heating pipes. A useful technique is to use the old pipes as pipe sleeves to protect new smaller bore pipes where they pass through walls and other masonry.

As time goes by it has to be admitted that there are fewer people with the skill to handle cast-iron repairs successfully so that there could well be increasing difficulty when anything does go wrong. It is well worthwhile searching for a company that has appropriate experience. Those who do not will tend to take the easy way out and recommend scrapping.

MODERN SYSTEMS

Radiators

These are the most common form of emitter. They are still available in cast-iron but the pressed steel panel types with or without convector fins attached are more generally used. The cheapest is the mass-produced panel type but radiators in cast-aluminium *etc*, though more expensive, may be justified because of specific features which will make them more technically suitable or visually acceptable in a particular application. NOTE: Most radiators are white when delivered though some companies offer options. This makes them very conspicuous especially in an older church. Do remember that any radiator can be painted any colour. Metallic finishes should be avoided because they reduce the emission from the radiator by a small percentage.

Another variation is the low surface temperature radiator in which the exposed surfaces are air cooled and are at a lower temperature than conventional radiators. Again these cost more than conventional panel types but they have their place where it is necessary to take precautions for young children or others who may need some protection from contact with surfaces that can reach about 80°C. The alternative is to fit wire guards. (See Chapter 10 – Safety).

Where panel radiators are installed on an outside wall it is useful to install a sheet of insulation behind them. Aluminium foil is sufficient. If being installed after the radiator is in position, one tip is to cut out a piece of hardboard a little smaller than the radiator with slots as necessary to fit over the supports, stick the foil onto the hardboard and wedge the whole against the wall. It is essential to leave airspace between the board and the radiator. This will reduce losses to the fabric in exchange for a small loss of output from the radiator.

Convectors

The simple convector is similar to the radiator except that the heating element may be a pipe mounted on a finned plate or simply a finned pipe within a casing. Most of these run at lower surface temperature than radiators. This reduces the radiant component of the heating.

Fan convectors

These comprise a bank of finned tubes inside a casing. A fan sucks air in from the room and forces it through the heater bank to warm the air and project it into the room.

These provide a very effective method of heating large spaces. The fan promotes good circulation and has the additional advantage of giving a lower temperature air outlet than can be achieved from a simple convector. This helps to reduce temperature variation between low and high levels in the building.

They are also extremely compact in relation to their output which makes them relatively easy to fit into a building such as a church with many existing restrictions.

For example, at the sacrifice of a couple of seats it is usually practicable to install one behind a pew front, operating through grilles covering slots cut out of the front. (See figure on page 28.)

They can also be encased in a properly designed wooden cabinet to match the adjacent furnishings.

Fan convectors can also be installed under floors, in ducts, or in the raised dais at the pulpit/communion table. These tend to suffer from limitations of access and are best avoided unless there is absolutely no alternative.

The fans in the best heaters of this type are of high quality and much quieter than those used in typical electric fan heaters. Provided that good quality heaters are installed the noise level at low speed should not be noticed. Higher speeds can be used before the service to heat the building. It is good practice to install a switch in a convenient location for the minister or church officer so that when absolute silence is

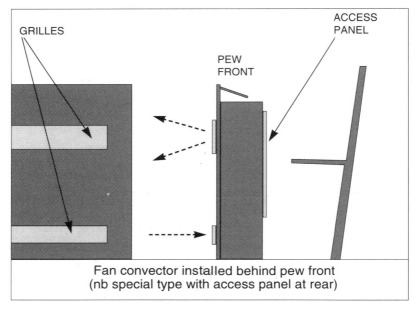

GRILLES

ACCESS PANEL

PEW FRONT

Fan convector installed behind pew front
(nb special type with access panel at rear)

required the heaters may be briefly switched off. An indicator light can be useful to avoid them being left switched off by accident.

These heaters should be fitted with low temperature fan cut-out switches to prevent operation of the fans when heat is not available and also two thermostats, one changing the fan from medium to low speed and the other simply on/off. The first should be set to operate a few degrees lower than the second.

Another advantage arises if a church building requires a small input of heat during the week. If water is circulated through heaters in the church when the hall is being heated, the output of the church heaters will be about 10% of normal. In this situation the fans would be controlled by time switch.

These units have some limitations for use in halls. As they circulate air from the room they will pick up dust and fluff in the filters which are fitted as standard. These are designed to be accessible for cleaning and this will need to be done at least twice a year in most halls. This does not arise in churches where typically once in five years should be adequate.

Pipe coils or radiators under pews

These are still a useful method of distributing heat exactly where it is needed. One 50mm pipe under each pew, or a loop of two 50mm pipes under alternate pews, is the maximum practical intensity of this type of heating.

A variation which may suit some situations is the use of small radiators (300mm high) which can also be fitted under pew seats. These are best used in the form of single panel or single panel plus one fin. Double panel radiators with or without fins give too high an output for the comfort of anyone sitting on the pew or in the pew behind. The higher output radiators can be used successfully along walls in place of old cast-iron pipes. In this case they may require guards to prevent anyone from sitting with their legs hard against them. This is more likely to arise than with pipes because of the greater potential area of contact. It is important to ensure that any protective arrangement does not interfere with the free flow of air over and above the radiators. Low surface temperature radiators or convectors are an alternative.

An advantage of using radiators is that all the work is within the daily experience of many heating engineers who do not have the experience to produce a well finished all-pipe installation.

Finned pipes

Industrial type heavy finned pipe with steel fins is useful in some applications. One 2″ pipe with fins can take the place of a pair of old 4″ CI pipes very successfully. The disadvantage is they are not very attractive in appearance even though they are available painted. They are best used in a situation where they can be screened while still allowing full air-circulation (not fully boxed in, there must be at least a generous gap at floor level and on the top of the box). They will need cleaning from time to time so it should be possible without too much trouble to get access for a brush or a powerful vacuum cleaner.

Other types of hot water emitter

Hot water can also be used for heated ceilings and floors. While these have attractions both from theoretical and artistic viewpoints, they do give practical problems both from the point of view of economy and maintenance. They should only be used where architectural requirements leave no practical option.

ADDING TO AN EXISTING SYSTEM

Analysis of an existing heating installation, especially an older one, may show that additional heating is required. Provided that the boiler has adequate spare capacity (or is due to be replaced and can be replaced with a larger one as necessary) it may be practicable to add more emitters to the existing system.

Disturbance of older cast-iron systems should be kept to a minimum. Where branches are required it is often preferable to try to use existing radiator or pipe connections. There is a form of coupling available which clamps round the pipe and involves no more than drilling a hole in the old pipe.

Heating engineers frequently overlook the difference in characteristics between old radiators and modern radiators or convectors. Most modern radiators are designed to operate on pumped systems and require more pressure differential than the old cast-iron units which originally ran on gravity systems.

If modern panel radiators are connected into an old system in place of cast-iron radiators, or added to the system, they normally do not heat properly from top to bottom and consequently output is reduced. This can also arise with a 'one-pipe' system where both connections to the radiator are from a single main pipe. This problem arises even when the system is pumped as is now general practice.

If a new radiator is being added to an old system, obtain a firm guarantee from the installer that the radiator will heat equally well over its whole surface. If, with the system fully heated, you can detect an appreciable difference in temperature between the top and the bottom with your hand, do not accept it.

A useful arrangement when adding modern radiators, convectors or fan convectors, is to establish a local pumped circuit — perhaps including some existing radiators. Connect the radiators *etc*, so that the water flows through each in sequence and add a small pump. The size of this pump can be calculated from technical data on heaters, but a domestic one will normally be adequate. Control the pump by a make-on-rise thermostat strapped to a local pipe on the main system. One valve on the circuit should be used by the heating engineer to balance the flow and it should be marked accordingly. Other valves should be removed or otherwise fixed fully open. The thermostat should be set to bring the pump into use when the circulating water temperature rises to, say, 40°C. (The use of the thermostat means that the electricity supply can be local rather than leading back to the boilerhouse.)

In some situations it may be more practicable to have all the additional emitters on a new separately pumped circuit from the boiler house.

CASE NOTES

Fan convectors in a hall where they had not been opened and cleaned for years, became completely ineffective. A powerful vacuum cleaner restored performance instantly. Fortunately in this case, the neglect of essential cleaning had not led to any damage to the motor.

In other cases motors have been ruined by overheating caused by an accumulation of dust and fluff and increased loading from a dirt-laden fan.

Numerous cases where modern panel radiators and even fan convectors have been added to old large bore or single pipe systems without proper consideration of design implications, as discussed above — leading to poor performance and disappointment.

There are many excellent examples of undersized old systems being upgraded by adding radiators or fan convectors in a technically correct manner at a fraction of the cost of a new system.

With many installations there is more heating than there need be in passageways, toilets, rooms that are now used as stores, and so on. The situation should be reviewed periodically and, if appropriate, the flow through these radiators reduced. The most permanent way of doing this is by means of the lockshield valves (*ie* those which cannot be adjusted without tools). This is best done by a heating engineer, particularly if there are motorised control valves in the system, as such radiators are sometimes used to provide a permanent small base load for the protection of boiler and pump.

A frequent need for bleeding radiators should not be accepted as normal. A heating engineer should be called in to investigate as it is often an indication of potential trouble. Switch off the boiler and pump before bleeding.

Running water at the ballcock in the header (expansion) tank indicates a leak. Fresh make-up water entering the system brings oxygen which encourages corrosion. These are often in an awkward position but should be checked.

When a pump has been added to an old gravity system it is often installed on a bypass pipe around an existing valve. The old pipe and valve are left so that if the pump fails the valve may be opened and the gravity system used until the pump has been repaired. It is surprising how often disappointing performance of a heating system has been found to be due to this valve being left partly or fully open. In this situation, the pump simply circulates water around the local circuit through the valve while the main system operates by gravity only. It is essential that when the pump is in use the valve must be closed.

⑤

HOT WATER CENTRAL HEATING – BOILERS

The boiler is the heart of the hot water central heating system. Provided that the rest of the system is looked after properly, it and its associated pump(s) and controls are the only items in a central heating system that should require replacement over a very long time.

Most are fuelled with gas or oil but there are also some electric boilers.

New boilers appear almost as regularly as new cars and it is usually claimed or implied that each new one has some advantage over the previous model. It is hardly ever worthwhile chasing after the latest development because the improvements in efficiency are generally small. In general, the time to change a boiler is when the existing one has deteriorated to such an extent that it or the burner is beyond economical repair or your insurance company has condemned it. Unfortunately only the latter is clear-cut and there will usually be different opinions under the first two headings. Old sectional cast-iron boilers can give good service for half a century with little loss of efficiency or deterioration in condition. (However, it is not now worthwhile converting them from oil to gas.) With modern lightweight boilers it is better to think in terms of a 20 year lifespan. The overall efficiency of an old boiler will be lower than that of a modern one principally because of the weight of metal and water to be heated. However, it is usually not worth changing for this reason alone as the savings generated will rarely justify the capital investment.

MULTIPLE BOILERS

Boilers used to be assembled on site. Now the general practice is to install a number of factory-assembled small boilers ('modular') to make up the full requirement. This is more convenient for the installer and has some advantages for the user, though these are often exaggerated.

A multiple boiler is no more efficient than a single boiler unless the installation and controls are properly designed in relation to the pattern of use of the heating system.

Multiple boilers *connected to a common flow and return* have only one advantage over a single boiler — if one fails you still have a proportion of heat from the others. This limitation applies even if the boilers are controlled electrically so that, say, one comes on for the church and one for the halls.

To make this into an *efficient* installation, controls must be added to ensure that heat is not wasted up the chimney by boilers that are not being fired. These controls cost money and are not usually offered by heating engineers for church installations when asked to quote for 'a boiler replacement', because it involves additional work and increased costs which are difficult to justify to a non-technical client in a competitive situation.

SEPARATE BOILERS FOR CHURCH AND HALLS

One of the simplest methods of achieving an economic boiler installation is to have separate boilers for the church and halls. Depending on relative sizes of the buildings and space within the boiler house the church 'boiler' might be two boilers connected in modular fashion. This is a very satisfactory arrangement because it means that for the church you have an automatic assurance that even if one boiler fails you will still have some heat. Depending on the size of the building you might use two boilers for the halls as well.

It also simplifies controls with independent time and temperature control for each system. Such an arrangement will cost less and almost certainly be more efficient than a fully engineered multi-boiler combination serving all areas with separate circuits and motorised valves. There will also be much less to go wrong in the future. It will cost very little more than the typical basic and relatively inefficient multi-boiler installation usually offered.

BOILER SIZE

While it is by no means a precise calculation, it is important to try to get a sensible relationship between the boiler output and the emission from the heat emitters installed.

The extremes of the situation are probably most noticeable in an older cast-iron system with a relatively high water content and used intermittently. The boiler must have a significant excess margin of output over the nominal heat emission from the installation because the nominal figure is based on the situation at working temperature (*ie* with the building fully heated). When you start up a boiler to heat a cold church in the middle of winter the surrounding air temperature may be very low indeed, and if the boiler output is low it can take a long time to build up water temperature and hence air temperature. During this period low grade heat soaks away into the fabric contributing little to eventual comfort. A correctly sized boiler will raise water, and consequently air temperature, more rapidly and at less cost because less heat will be dissipated prior to occupation.

On the other hand, if an excessively large boiler is applied to an older cast-iron system it can destroy the installation surprisingly quickly. This is due to the temperature of the water rising very quickly and leading to expansion at a rate which the pipework cannot adjust to. This causes stress which demonstrates itself by the development of leaks at joints. As these are repaired others develop, until everyone throws up their hands in horror and scraps what could have been a perfectly good system if it had been treated more thoughtfully. This is a more common problem than is generally realized.

With modern low water content heating systems it is general practice to cut down margins to a minimum as this is good for economy in normal situations. In the case of intermittently heated churches it is preferable to maintain a significant margin and have a control system which will ensure that the boiler does not fire unnecessarily. (See Chapter 9 for further information.)

One of the main causes of this wrong sizing was a convention that was adopted for new church buildings sometime around the '50s and '60s to the effect that, for churches, a boiler ought to have double the output of the heating system. Since buildings of that period were generally church/hall complexes, it meant that during the week, with only halls being heated, the boiler was grossly oversized. For new churches with steel pipework this was inefficient but did not do any damage. When the same rule of thumb is applied to replacement boilers for older systems, it can be destructive.

The following are not intended as design figures but rather as guidance to help with assessing heating engineers' proposals for boilers. The base figure should be the total emission load connected to the boiler. You probably will not have this figure unless you are being quoted for a complete heating system, but a fair approximation can be made by using the figure obtained in the calculations to be found in Chapter 10.

(1) A maximum of 50% margin in any circumstances.
(2) If heating a church only with an old cast-iron system – 30% to 50%.
(3) Heating a hall only – 20/25%.
(4) If heating a church/hall complex with an old cast-iron system from a single boiler installation, a maximum of 20% of total to reduce speed of temperature increase when heating either church or halls alone. (It is preferable to have separate boilers which will allow for the appropriate margin in each case.)

A simple device for restricting the rate of temperature increase where there are two modular boilers is to have a delay timer so that the second boiler does not start for, say, half an hour to one hour after the first. This can easily be fitted retrospectively if necessary.

CONDENSING BOILERS

The only currently available boiler which gives a significant advance in efficiency is the condensing boiler.

It is only available for gas firing. In essence, these boilers extract more heat out of the hot gases before they pass to the flue by adding more heating surface. This allows the temperature of the gases to drop to a point where the moisture condenses out and is drained off (hence 'Condensing'). Because of the need for drains to remove the condensation there may be difficulty and added expense when installing these boilers in underground boiler houses.

The increase in efficiency is likely to be of the order of eight to ten per cent. The boiler costs more and will have about the same life span as a conventional boiler so that the more it is used the better the economic case for installation (*eg* it will generally be more useful for a halls boiler than a church one).

At the time of writing they have not yet become very popular. Few heating engineers have significant experience of them and they do not tend to be offered to a contractor anxious to put in a low price. It will probably be necessary to specifically ask for a quote based on this type of boiler.

If you already have running costs for an existing boiler and it is only the boiler that is being changed, it is fairly easy to assess the benefit. It can be expected to be of the order of eight to ten per cent of the existing gas heating bill. It is a case of relating this to the extra capital cost and deciding if you feel it is justified.

COMBI BOILERS

This is another significant new development. These boilers really belong to the domestic field but the larger units can be used where there is a hall/kitchen/toilets area which is not too large. The advantages are that they can be fixed on a wall with a flue through the wall, require no chimney, expansion or other tank in the loft, and provide as much domestic hot water as needed without the need for a storage tank. (They stop supplying heat to the central heating system while providing domestic hot water, but this will not be noticed.) They are fairly complex and must be expected to require more maintenance (at higher costs) in the long run, but they can provide a relatively low cost installation in the first place because of savings in labour charges.

OTHER GAS BOILERS

Apart from the above there are two basic types: the atmospheric burner type (as most domestic boilers are) or the blown gas burner (with a separate burner in front like an oil fired boiler).

The atmospheric burner type is generally to be preferred in church applications because there is less to go wrong with it and it will normally be quieter in operation, which can be important. The blown gas unit may sometimes have an advantage if the chimney size is small. The volume of flue gas to be handled is less for a given output rating because no draught divertor is required. Draught divertors induce fresh air into flue gases as they pass to the chimney.

Atmospheric burners usually have pilot burners for ignition. These consume a little gas while they are in use (typically 2000kWh = 70 therms per annum). They should be turned off during the summer. Some makers give the option of an automatic piezo igniter which does away with the need for the pilot to be running all the time, but at a higher initial cost. This is of most benefit when the running hours are least *ie* an independently heated church.

OIL BOILERS

These tend to be installed now where there is no gas available or the cost of a supply is judged to be too high. This is in spite of an economic situation that has for many years clearly favoured the oil-fired boiler!

The capital cost of a gas boiler and necessary associated costs (meter kiosk, gas piping, chimney lining, *etc*) is nearly always greater than a replacement oil-fired boiler. Furthermore, in recent years the running cost of gas, with brief exceptions, has been appreciably more than oil in quantities used by typical churches.

The positive advantages of gas over oil are convenience, cleanliness, and lower maintenance costs. With the exception of the new condensing boilers, which are only applicable to gas, there is no practical difference in terms of effectiveness or efficiency between the two.

ELECTRIC BOILERS

Electric boilers were installed at one time in many churches replacing old coal or oil-fired boilers. They are not a cost effective method of heating a church or hall.

There are two types of electric boiler: (1) the immersion type which has a series of elements inside a cylinder and (2) the electrode type where there are three electrodes (one per phase) projecting down into the water, and current flows between them to heat the water. This type are always in vertical cylinder form with a hand-wheel to adjust the setting of the electrodes. In the context of church heating, certain characteristics of the latter make it even less efficient than the former. There are very few still in use.

There have been developments in the application of electric boilers which incorporate insulated storage tanks to hold water heated at the lowest rates for use at other times, but these are not practical in typical church, or church hall, applications.

You get twice as good value for money spent on electricity by using direct electric heaters. (See Chapter 6 which discusses this further.)

However, there is a capital cost involved in changing and when this is taken into account the decision may be to carry on and accept the higher cost. If the existing installation is undersized and there is spare capacity in the supply cable, it can be useful to install some direct heaters to be used in parallel with the boiler system to shorten the total preheat period and obtain some economy. This can be quite a low capital exercise which would recover outlay in a relatively short time.

COAL BOILERS

These are now very rare and are not usually economical in a typical set of intermittently used church buildings. Even the most automatic requires more attention than gas or oil.

MULTI FUEL/WOOD/STRAW BURNING BOILERS

The question of the suitability of these arises from time to time and the answer must be that they need a reliable and cheap supply of fuel *plus* a guarantee that for the next 20 years you will have a succession of people who are prepared to devote themselves to the operation of the boiler. The latter is the real problem.

OPERATIONAL NOTES

Oil fired cast-iron boilers will generally last longer (typically about five years) than steel boilers in a church context.

If a boiler is operated at 60°C (140°F) the output of the installed system is only 60% of what it would be at the standard maximum of 82°C (180°F). This is quite often found to be at the root of a complaint of low temperatures. This fact also has its uses, as will be discussed in Chapter 9.

Each gas boiler has a rated output and a rated input. The final test to be carried out in most manufacturer's instructions is to run the boiler and check the gas flow by means of the meter to see that it is in line with the stated figure. Installers often omit or disregard the results of this test.

The following check is much easier than may appear at first sight!

The input figure is quoted in kW (and in Btu per hour). The gas meter measures input in cubic feet. To complicate things the calorific value of gas is now quoted as megajoules per cubic metre (MJ/m^3).

The easiest way to check the gas flow rate is to start with the INPUT figure quoted on the boiler in kW, *eg* 85kW. Then convert this to cubic feet per hour: 85 × 127 ÷ calorific value of gas (in megajoules per cubic metre, *eg* 38) = 284 cub. ft. per hour. (Calorific value varies and it is always quoted on your gas bill. Use the latest for any check. Typical values are 38 to 40 MJ/m^3.)

On the gas meter is a small dial with figures at the top and bottom and a red hand. The larger of the two figures is the number of cubic feet per revolution of the small hand. With a stop watch (preferably), measure the time for a complete revolution and then calculate the hourly rate thus: cubic feet per revolution ÷ time in seconds for one revolution × 3600 = cub. ft. per hour.

If the boiler is correctly set these two figures should be within ten per cent of each other. If the actual figure is more than five per cent up you will certainly be wasting money because the excess will simply be increasing the losses up the chimney. If more than five per cent under you will be losing output from the boiler. This may not matter too much if the heating is satisfactory. If the figure is more than ten per cent down then questions should be put to the service engineer because not only is output less than it should be but the reduced heat input can lead to corrosion of boiler surfaces and shortening of the life of the boiler.

Pilot burner failure is often caused by an inadequate gas supply situation. The correction of incorrect gas flow is usually straightforward but must only be undertaken by a qualified technician. There can never be a good reason for a high setting, but there may be an important reason for a low one.

As an example, a contractor may have installed boilers which were too large for the chimney. This might only be discovered when the boilers were started up. Faced with this situation, the contractor may have lowered the input (and consequently the output), thus reducing the flue gas flow from the boilers. To attempt to increase the gas flow in such circumstances could be dangerous.

Another cause of low gas flow is that the contractor has put in too small a pipe between the meter and the boiler. The only cure in this case is to fit the right size of pipe.

Again there are cases where the main British Gas supply pipe and meter are not big enough to handle the demand of the boiler because no one has seen fit to advise British Gas of an increased demand. A responsible contractor should have kept you right on this at the time of installation.

The most useful time to check gas flow is immediately after the boiler has been installed and before final payment to the contractor.

The output of oil-fired boilers is determined by a combination of oil jet size and oil pump pressure. There is no ready way for the user to check.

An immersion type electric boiler can be simply checked from the electric meter with nothing else on. With the boiler and system cold, run the boiler for exactly an hour taking meter readings before and after. This will give its hourly consumption which should equal the rating marked on the boiler. If it is significantly less it will indicate that one or more elements need replacing.

AIR SUPPLY

It is essential that any boiler burning oil, gas or other fuel should have adequate air supply. This is an important safety matter especially with gas boilers. There are specific requirements for ventilation and the installation instruction book issued with your boiler will state the minimum cross-sectional area required. If you have any doubt ask your service engineer. This should be checked at the time of installation. It is very important not to block up any built-in ventilators to reduce draughts. Equipment stored in a boiler house can find its way in front of a ventilator. Autumn leaves can block a ground-level ventilator. Vents are sometimes deliberately blocked because a pilot light goes out when the real problem is low gas pressure (see above).

PIPE INSULATION

All hot pipes in the boiler house should be insulated, as should distribution pipes which are not serving also as heat emitters. (Most of these will be out of sight.)

PUMPS

Pumps are an essential part of all modern systems. There may still be a few old systems without them. Provided they are selected with care and are no larger or more powerful than necessary, they will do no harm and can actually reduce the stresses on the old system by giving a more even and progressive rate of increase of temperature.

FEED AND EXPANSION TANKS AND SEALED PRESSURISED SYSTEMS

In general, hot water systems have a feed and expansion tank to take care of changes in the volume of water in heating and cooling. These should be checked periodically as they are often in a tower or other out of the way place. Your service engineer will probably not normally check. They have ball valves that can stick and pipes that can get gummed up with possibly disastrous consequences.

There is an alternative that is being used more frequently. This is the sealed pressurised system. The main advantage of this is that it eliminates the need for a high level tank. It can be very useful in cases where there is a problem in finding a suitable location for a tank. However, care must be taken when using such a system on an older cast-iron installation as it can cause leaks by producing too high a pressure. It is very much a matter for which the heating engineer is responsible. He must make certain that the pressure does not exceed that produced by the original header tank by ensuring that the new tank has adequate capacity for the expansion of the water in the system, fitting all necessary safety devices *and* checking that all settings are correct *before* commissioning.

WATER TREATMENT

The water in the system should be treated with a proprietary corrosion inhibitor. This is particularly important with more modern systems. When a system has been drained down it needs to be replaced.

SERVICING

Regular boiler cleaning and servicing is essential for safety and to maintain efficiency. The minimum requirement is an annual visit.

It is useful to have a service contract, if only because of the discipline that this introduces. You must have a written document and be aware of what is being checked. Cleaning is usually included for modern boilers but is often not covered for older units. Sometimes only the boiler is covered and pumps and controls may be neglected. Insurance inspections are only concerned with the physical condition of the items covered. Every operational part of the system needs to be checked by someone.

For boilers with blown gas and pressure jet oil burners, an efficiency check should be asked for. This is the only proper confirmation that settings are correct. In the case of atmospheric gas boilers, provided the gas flow is right everything else should normally be satisfactory.

Water should be checked for corrosion inhibitor level and topped up as necessary.

CASE NOTES

Complete destruction of cast iron heating system in church and halls due to installation of oversized boilers.

Death of a beadle in a small, poorly ventilated boiler house in the days when the boiler was coal fired. Apparently he used to have a seat in the warm boiler house to read his paper after he had stoked up early on a Sunday morning. There will still be boiler houses with modern boilers where this could happen.

Many cases of poor heating are due to undersizing of replacement boilers and also to inadequate gas supply to boilers. Many of the latter were easily remedied.

Deteriorating performance of a heating system may be due to a worn pump.

Dirty boilerhouses are usually also inefficient.

6

DIRECT ELECTRIC HEATING

Direct electric heating is very important in church buildings. Many churches and halls, especially smaller buildings in rural areas, are heated in this way.

Apart from its use as a main source of heat, it can also be useful as a supplement to hot water or warm air systems and as an alternative to central heating when only a small hall or room needs to be heated.

It is a characteristic of electric heating that it requires little attention and is usually maintenance free for many years, a point often overlooked in comparing running costs with other forms of heating. (See note in Chapter 3 regarding testing.)

The economics of electric heating are related to tariffs. In many cases the requirements of a church/hall combination fit in well with an 'Evening and Weekend' tariff. Some 'off-peak' tariffs which give supply at mutually acceptable periods during the day may be applicable and economical. The cost of electricity at full standard commercial rate will generally be such as to make it relatively very expensive.

In considering installing electric heating or extending existing heating it is important at an early stage to determine the probable total load and discuss with the appropriate supply company. In rural areas in particular there may be considerable capital costs incurred in obtaining an increased supply.

TUBULAR HEATERS

This is by far the most common electric heater used in churches. They have been used for about 60 years, have been installed in hundreds of churches and are a very satisfactory method of putting heat just where it is needed. Care has to be taken in locating them so that the possibility of physical contact is reduced to a minimum.

It is generally not possible to install sufficient tubes under pews to make up the total heat requirement of the church, and additional heaters, of appropriate type, are needed elsewhere. Tubular heaters used to be available in very long lengths but are now generally available at a maximum length of 1.8m and each requires a separate fused spur outlet.

Many units installed 50 or more years ago are still giving satisfactory service. Their performance does not deteriorate progressively. As with most electric heaters operating primarily as convectors, they either heat or they do not.

Tubular heaters have quite a high surface temperature. The makers advise the use of guards, but those available are not usually of a completely satisfactory design for underpew application. With the normal type of pew support found in Scotland there are front and back legs connected to cross members on the floor and under the seat. Wire guards can only be used if the heaters are mounted on the floor and in that location they are soon damaged by feet. The guard is pressed against the heater and becomes ineffective. The whole arrangement becomes a dirt-trap which cannot be cleaned.

Because of this it has been the practice to omit guards when the tubes are fixed under pews in normally inaccessible positions. The safest position is with the tube centre about 150mm below the seat with the mountings screwed on to the back of the front upright. In that location it requires a deliberate action to make contact with them.

In addition, or alternatively, if it is impracticable to fix the tubes as suggested, a neat guard can be formed using single light wooden battens fitted to pew supports in locations which will prevent any possibility of contact in the normal course of events. It is important to allow a free flow of air at bottom and top and to leave access for cleaning. They can be finished to match the pews.

Another precaution would be a small sticker attached to the bookboard of each pew saying something like: 'DO NOT TOUCH TUBULAR HEATER UNDER PEW'.

Children used to remain seated during services, but reports suggest an increasing tendency for them to crawl about under pews. If this is regarded as a possibility it should be taken into account.

These heaters do not have any built-in temperature control or safety cut-out arrangement. This makes it very important that they should never be installed in a position where clothing, curtains, *etc*, could lie on top of them.

A variation on the tubular heater has the trade name 'Tuvec'. They are of angular construction and have about twice the output of a conventional tubular heater of the same length. They are available in single, double and triple units up to 2.5m long and are very suitable for use at low level, *eg* on walls, taking the place of the original cast iron pipes. Where pews run to walls on which these heaters are fixed it will be possible for people sitting in the pew to touch them with their legs or clothing and therefore guards are essential. A very satisfactory design can be ordered with the heaters. As with tubular heaters these do not have any built-in temperature control or safety cut-out arrangement.

SKIRTING CONVECTOR HEATERS

This is similar in many respects to the Tuvec heater except that it comes in standard units each 800mm long and with 500watt output. They can be made up in multiples and are subject to the same limitations.

LOW TEMPERATURE PANEL HEATERS

Low temperature panel heaters are available for fixing on the back of pews, radiating gentle heat over the person in the pew behind. These have been used to a limited extent. There have been problems in a few instances with earlier models. Only those with BEAB approval should now be installed. These are fitted with approved automatic cut-outs and the surface temperature is controlled at a level which obviates the need for guards. They are often white and the use of alternative finishes could usefully be investigated.

They are now relatively expensive in terms of pounds per kilowatt installed compared with other electric heaters, but have useful applications particularly for local heating, typically in a large church with a small congregation. In such a case the existing heating or alternative heaters can be used to give a lower level of general heating, while regularly used pews (plus a few extra for visitors) can be fitted with these local heaters.

They also have applications, mounted on walls or screens to give local supplementary heating for organists and choir members who are sometimes less well-catered for than the rest of the congregation because of their location. They are also very suitable as pulpit heaters.

CONVECTOR HEATERS (*without fans*)

This embraces a very wide selection of heaters and unit prices. Many are available either as portable or wall-mounted units. Portable heaters have their uses, but for permanent installations wall mounted is always preferable. Most have thermostats and safety cut outs. Some have built in time switches or one hour timers. They provide a convenient relatively low cost heat source in units up to 3kW.

However, while all will be suitable for use in rooms of typical domestic size, many are unsuitable for use in halls. This is because of the design of thermostatic control. Where this is built into the body of the heater with no external sensor it is often found that the thermostat is influenced by the temperature of the heater rather than solely by room temperature. This leads to the convector switching off while the temperature of the hall is still well below requirement making it difficult to raise temperature to a comfortable level.

Thus, in a hall which may be calculated as requiring 16kW (say 8 × 2kW convectors) it can be found that individual heaters begin to switch off and on within a relatively short time of starting so that the effective input may be reduced to only about 8kW. The consequence is at worst completely ineffective heating, and at best an extension of the pre-occupation heating period and increased running costs. This can be particularly serious where electricity is on the 'Evening and Weekend' tariff where it may be found necessary to use an excessive amount of electricity at the high rate to be comfortable for an evening meeting.

As a general rule any heaters proposed for such applications should be checked by running one in the hall (or in a comparable situation) to check the behaviour of the thermostat. This should be done before buying the full quantity required. Existing heaters should be checked.

The best type of convector for the purpose is one with an external sensor for the thermostat. This is usually mounted between the casing and the wall or at the very bottom of the casing. These tend to be the most expensive convectors.

Built in thermostats should be set and locked about mid position initially. Some fine adjustment may be needed with experience but they should never be left free or set to maximum. The facility to cover or lock the thermostat is a point to check when considering a heater.

In certain cases where new wiring is being installed for additional electric heating, capital cost can be kept down at a slight loss in comfort by using low cost convectors and bypassing the existing thermostats in such a way as not to interfere with the safety cut out arrangements. The complete circuit can then be controlled by a single thermostat through a contactor. The installation contractor would advise on comparative costs. This principle can also be applied to existing installations where the thermostats are causing a problem.

While useful in some particular cases, built-in time switches are generally both inconvenient and a waste of money because the time switch is usually 24-hour and does not operate if switched off at the socket.

A built-in timer which can be set at anything up to an hour has advantages in certain applications where a short heating period is needed and there is a danger of the heater being left on accidentally.

FAN HEATERS

There are many types ranging from the small portable to the over-door downward projection unit. They are generally an effective means of producing heat quickly from a relatively compact source. The main problem with virtually all of them is that if they are not noisy when new they become so after a year or two. There are exceptions, but as a general rule they are to be avoided where reasonable quietness is needed; and this includes the church and often halls though they have their uses, mounted fairly high on the walls of small halls with low headroom and occupied mainly by young children. (Radiant heaters are also suitable if the ceiling is high enough.)

The over-door downward projection heater is often referred to as an air curtain and fails to live up to the expectations suggested by the term. An air curtain is quite a specialized and expensive device which forms a positive screen across an opening and stops air movement through it.

The normal type of heater installed over doors projects a stream of warm air downwards but this dissipates rapidly and you will generally find that below about waist level it has no practical influence on the situation. They can be useful in church vestibules but they are better mounted on the outside of inner doors rather than on the inside of outer doors. In the first case the heat is either carried into the church or makes a contribution to the comfort of office bearers, but in the latter much of it is immediately lost outside.

It is not generally a good idea to mount them inside the church though there are exceptions where the vestibule is very small or non-existent and office bearers greet arrivals inside the church. The difficulty is that the noise inside the church may be found to be intrusive even though the heaters are switched off before commencement of the service.

RADIANT (INFRA-RED) HEATERS

Where there is sufficient headroom these can be very useful in halls where they have the particular advantage of being up out of harm's way. They are rather less so in churches. Pews tend to block the radiant heat from a local source and there can be difficulty with legs and feet. They can, however, be used very successfully in conjunction with under-pew heating or with low temperature panels in pews.

They are also useful in vestibules where they will generally be found more effective and economical than fan heaters.

In general it is better not to attempt to have thermostatic control with this type of heater. People are conscious of excessive radiant heat and generally respond by switching some heaters off as necessary. For this reason it is a good idea to have an on/off or full/half switch convenient to each heater.

RADIANT QUARTZ HEATERS

These are relatively new and are based on the use of tungsten halogen lamps enclosed in a filter to reduce the intensity of light. They operate at very high temperature and the beam of heat can be controlled by reflectors into fairly narrow beams. They are very suitable in churches without pews, but in some cases have been less successful where there are pews because they block the direct heat from the legs and feet. There are also problems in using them under galleries or anywhere else that headroom is restricted when the beam may be too powerful especially when the congregation is standing. (Manufacturer's figures for *minimum* mounting height should generally be treated with caution.)

Early models had a rather distinctive rosy glare. There have been progressive improvements by using, for example, softer filters and gold coloured reflectors, the most recent development being a neutral filter which will have visual advantages for some applications.

One disadvantage with all radiant heaters is that to be effective they have to be located where they can be seen. The light from the quartz lamps is quite bright and concentrated and it is sometimes not easy to find suitable locations.

The heaters can be fairly bulky and there is a wide variety of designs from the acceptable to those which belong only in the factory. Experience suggests that the use of a linear arrangement of lamps is more visually acceptable than the larger type of unit with say three lamps arranged vertically. They cost much more than infra-red heaters of the same output.

In the case of halls it is important to remember that lamps are very expensive to replace so that they need to be protected from some of the more energetic activities of youth organisations.

It is useful to arrange switching which allows selection of, say, low, medium and full heating from any group of lamps. Automatic thermostatic control and dimming facilities are available.

It is advisable to allow for a contactor and time switch as under typical winter conditions it will be necessary to switch on at least an hour before occupation. This can increase to about three hours under severe conditions as it is necessary to have some heat in the fabric if people are to feel comfortable.

While these heaters may be used to give light by exposing some of the length of one lamp in each fitting or by use of a lamp for light only, it should be noted that this gives a very intense light source which may not be very satisfactory.

STORAGE HEATERS

These are not suitable for heating churches or halls except in certain very special circumstances. Even on the lowest rates they tend to be very expensive to run because there is a lot of heat produced when it is of no use.

Generally, the only practical application is where there is an office which is in use most days and where standard rate electricity has to be used as the main heat source. Under these circumstances the installation of a storage heater may make it practicable to change to the 'Evening and Weekend' tariff for all electricity.

CEILING HEATING

This is rarely used now largely because early installations did not use enough insulation above the elements in the ceilings and proved relatively expensive to run. Properly designed it has its place in certain situations.

FLOOR HEATING

Electric floor heating was installed in many new churches over a period. Few survived for many years. The heating was imbedded in concrete and was very slow to respond which made it unsuitable for intermittently heated buildings. Things went wrong with the concrete, corroding the elements, and sections of heating were lost. In other cases there was flooding which played havoc with the installation.

ELECTRIC HEATERS FOR SUPPLEMENTARY HEATING

With any form of heating which is undersized and consequently taking too long to heat up, electric convectors can be used as backup within the limits of the existing electric circuits.

If new circuits are needed, then it will be practicable to also consider radiant heaters at high level. These can be particularly useful or improve conditions in the central area occupied by the communion table and the choir found in many churches which do not have a chancel. For a variety of reasons this area is frequently inadequately heated.

It is a good idea to have permanent supplementary heating on a time switch so that it can be programmed to come on a couple of hours before the service.

It should not be forgotten that in a church which is not regularly full, convector heaters can often be fixed to the back of a pew, losing one or two seats but avoiding the need to cut away pews to find space.

PROBLEMS

The most common fault is undersizing. With direct electric heating this can lead to higher than necessary costs because this type of heating is only economical if conditions in a church can be made comfortable in not more than about three hours for normal mid winter conditions (about an hour for a hall). If shortage of heating makes it necessary to put heating on overnight, then there is almost certainly a significant degree of undersizing and waste. In such a case it will usually pay to add some convectors or radiant heaters to boost the heat input and allow shorter times to be used.

The performance of reflectors on radiant heaters can deteriorate with time. In most cases it is practicable to clean them. Appropriate safety precautions should be taken and manufacturer's instructions followed.

DESIGN OF CHURCH SYSTEMS

All of the heaters discussed above, with the possible exception of storage heaters, have their place in church heating systems.

Each has its limitations which have been noted and need to be taken into account.

If changing to direct electric heating there is a case for removing the old cast-iron pipes. This facilitates the location of new heaters and also removes a very cold item from the church.

DESIGN OF HALL SYSTEMS

For larger halls, especially those used by active youth organizations, there is a case for radiant heating. There is advantage in using infra-red rather than radiant quartz heating in terms of capital and long term element/lamp replacement costs. In practice there is not as much difference in electricity cost as is sometimes inferred.

For smaller halls which are primarily used for meetings a higher standard of comfort will be obtained with convector heaters.

LOCAL FROST PROTECTION

With direct electric and gas heating, and even in some cases where there is central heating, there are places such as toilets and kitchens which need local heating for frost protection. These should always be controlled by a tamper-proof froststat set about 5°C (or slightly higher). Small tubular heaters are suitable. There are other heaters with built-in thermostats/froststats which may cost less to install and serve as ordinary heaters when required but with greater risk of being left on accidentally.

SAFETY

In all cases where alterations or additions to an electrical installation are being made it is essential that a competent electrician is employed, as an unqualified person can easily overlook factors essential to safety and fire protection.

⑦
DIRECT GAS HEATING

This can be very economical and energy efficient given the right situation. With some exceptions most heaters have been designed in the first place for industrial applications and adapted for church and hall use. Running costs are low if on mains gas, but LPG (tanks and bottles) can be expensive and only really justified where there is difficulty with other energy sources.

Safe access for repair and maintenance is very important and must be taken into account at the design stage.

FLUELESS GAS HEATERS

This includes radiant plaque heaters, convectors and portable bottled gas heaters. All of these have been used in churches and halls but their application is very limited. Because the products of combustion are discharged directly into the atmosphere, very good ventilation is essential. Condensation can be a serious problem and can destroy decoration surprisingly quickly, particularly in an intermittently heated building. As a general rule, these heaters should not be used in new projects. Where they are in use consideration should be given to replacing them with alternative heating.

GAS RADIANT TUBE HEATERS

These are not extensively used but have potential in specific situations because of low capital cost and low running cost. They consist of black metal tubes with an aluminium reflector above and are of strictly functional appearance. They are mounted at high level. They are rather more suited to buildings without galleries.

Combustion products can and must be exhausted outside the building. (See note above regarding flueless gas heaters.) Limitations are in appearance and the noise from fans, burners and expansion/contraction. Some manufacturers have gone to considerable lengths to reduce noise to a level which has been accepted in churches. Temperature control is usually on/off for each unit and this can make it difficult to maintain an even temperature especially with a small number of heaters or if all heaters are controlled by a single thermostat.

Heaters of this type can provide a useful supplement to an undersized central heating system. In such a situation the gas heaters might be used as the sole source of heat at the beginning and end of the season.

BALANCED FLUE GAS CONVECTORS

These are a practical and flexible form of heater. The main limitation is the need to install them on an outside wall, though there are some — relatively expensive — units which can be installed a short distance from the wall. Each unit needs a hole drilled through the wall and a terminal and guard outside. Air for combustion comes in and products of combustion go out through the flue inserted in this hole. (There are situations where these external projections may be felt to be visually undesirable. They have also been known to attract the attention of vandals.)

Units tend to be relatively bulky. If pews are against the wall it will probably be necessary to cut some back. If aisles are against the wall the heaters will reduce the width. Where there are small children some may require guards because of surface temperature, though fan assisted units have lower surface temperature and are also preferable for larger or higher buildings.

They require a higher capital outlay than radiant tube heaters and a little more in running costs. It is only necessary to use heaters as required and this flexibility and consequent relatively high overall efficiency makes for lower fuel costs than central heating. Temperature control is generally good. If control is by flame modulation noise level will probably not be noticeable, but on/off control, especially if associated with spark ignition and a fan, may be found to be intrusive especially in a church.

Older balanced flue gas convectors probably have to be controlled manually but new models can be controlled by time switch and, if required, central thermostat control. Some units have thermostatic control in an accessible position. There can be difficulty in ensuring that these are not interfered with.

INDIRECT WARM AIR – UNIT HEATERS

These are intended for moderately high level mounting inside the area to be heated. They comprise a compact gas-fired heat exchanger and a fan which recirculates the air in the hall through the heater. Products of combustion are exhausted outside. Unit heaters tend to be noisy and unsightly and are generally limited to games halls which are not high enough to accommodate radiant tubes. (NOTE: In some situations the air flow could deflect shuttlecocks! This may be more acceptable than radiant tubes which melt them if they land on top of the reflector.)

INDIRECT WARM AIR – DUCTED

This is a larger type of heater operating on the same principle as the unit heater and located in a separate chamber (or outside) with warm air distributed and returned by duct. More generally applicable, but for practical reasons they are usually limited to situations where this type of heating has been designed into the original building. There can be a noise problem if the unit is too close to an occupied area.

DIRECT WARM AIR SYSTEM

The heater comprises a fan, gas burners, and controls. Air is drawn from outside, warmed by burning gas in the airstream, and blown into the building, slightly pressurising the interior and forcing air out through ventilators and gaps in the fabric. It is essential that leakage is not excessive or it may be difficult to heat the building. Timber-lined ceilings are one example, where small gaps between timbers, caused by drying out over the years, may not be visible, but may add up to a considerable cross sectional area.

Sophisticated controls maintain even temperature and ensure that the whole arrangement is safe. Condensation within the building is not a problem though moisture will be deposited where the air temperature drops to its dew point. (This is a factor that should not be treated lightly because it is possible that the condensation will occur in a place that is out of sight and inaccessible. It is advisable to discuss the use of this type of heating with an architect, preferably one who knows the building.) Design detail is important, to avoid excessive temperature differential and noise levels. For this reason it is advisable to deal with a specialist company.

Because of the relative costs, this system is at its most economically attractive when the building is used frequently.

ADDITIONAL GENERAL POINTS

Provided that the equipment is regularly serviced by competent people there should be little in the way of problems, but note that servicing is a significant recurring cost because each unit needs attention. Access, especially for high level radiant tubes, must be planned before installation.

If the building is a church and if it contains a pipe organ, flags or other valuable or historic material, it would be advisable to take advice from the organ builder or other appropriate person on all of the above with the exception of balanced flue convectors.

NEW INSTALLATIONS

All direct gas heaters with the possible exception of balanced flue gas convectors have characteristics with which those accustomed to hot water central heating may not be familiar and may not like, at least initially. With all direct gas systems, and particularly if it is church heating that is being considered, it is preferable that some of those concerned should attend a service in a church with similar heating so that they can form their own opinion.

CASE NOTES

A large church with mosaic tiling in the chancel installed plaque type flueless gas heaters. Condensation from the heaters caused tiles to fall out of the mosaic. Fortunately the original central heating had been retained so it was recommissioned with a new boiler and the flueless heating relegated to standby use.

A church installation of balanced flue gas convectors with fans where the noises produced by the on/off operation of the burner and fans under thermostatic control was more noticeable than expected. This sort of thing is not apparent from catalogues or from a demonstration and illustrates the importance of trying to attend a service in a church with the same type of heating.

The same sort of situation has occurred with radiant tube heaters.

(8)

CONTROLS IN GENERAL

No heating apart from an open fire or solid fuel stove can be used without automatic controls of some form. Even the most basic electric and gas heating appliances are protected with safety controls such as a fuse or a flame failure device.

Controls are used for safety, for temperature control and for time control. They also control energy use usually as a by-product of the way in which they control temperature and time.

With all time and temperature controls it is important to note some general facts.

A contractor will usually set up controls to arbitrary figures when he installs them. When commissioned they need checking to ensure that they are connected and functioning properly and then correctly adjusted. It would be unusual for a contractor to be in a position to get all settings right in the short time he can afford to spend on this. It is important to make certain that they are functioning before accepting the installation and that the necessary information is available to allow you to make further adjustments in the light of experience. Instruction manuals should be handed over. If the installation is other than of the simplest there is probably also the need for a written explanation of the adjustment facilities available and how these interact with each other.

Calibrations on thermostats can only be taken as a guide. Final settings should be arrived at by experiment and refined with practical experience.

Church heating controls are generally looked after by a church officer or a volunteer who will have many other things to attend to. Those responsible for maintenance within the congregation change and it is unlikely that they will have any understanding of controls. There is a very strong case for simplicity rather than seeking the ultimate in control through sophistication. Experience suggests that after about five years it is hard to find anyone who understands a sophisticated system or can even recognize a fault.

If sophisticated controls are specified, the installer may well have no experience beyond your installation and the nearest maker's expert may be a hundred or two expensive miles away. After a few years the usual end product is a situation which is less energy efficient than a simpler and more easily understood system would have been.

For this reason there will be no discussion of Building Energy Management Systems. There are many of these to choose from. They are essentially computer controlled and given a suitable installation can achieve useful results at a cost. However they come into the same category as straw-fired boilers – before you install you should satisfy yourself that you will have a guaranteed supply of dedicated supervisors for the next 20 years!

This is a rapidly developing field and it is reasonable to expect that the really simple-to-operate practical unit is not many years away. Probably the best long term advice is to avoid the products pressed on you by salesmen claiming dramatic guaranteed savings without even having seen your installation, and take the advice of a heating engineer or independent consultant after a study of your precise requirements.

SAFETY CONTROLS

Safety controls will not be dealt with here to any extent. They are essentially the responsibility of the equipment manufacturer and the installer who have to meet the requirements of standard specifications, regulations and codes of practice appropriate to the equipment. Any responsible person servicing equipment should check safety devices.

The main points to be made here are that the user should not interfere with or adjust safety controls.

Examples of interference or neglect which have been seen are:

(1) pieces of ordinary wire used in place of fuses;
(2) thermal fuse links controlling oil cut-off valves being replaced with

wires and cut-off valves held open with a piece of wire tied round
a convenient projection. (NOTE: In an emergency a piece of string
is a safe temporary expedient.);

(3) gas and oil boilers operating under the control of thermostats where
the sensor has been moved out of position and is ineffective.

Older equipment should be suspect. Safety requirements have increased
over the years and older equipment may not have the same degree of
built-in protection.

Among electric heaters, tubular heaters, skirting heaters, older panel
heaters and many radiant heaters do not have any built-in safety
controls. If any of these are in positions where, for example, a coat laid
over a pew, could come in contact with an unguarded heater or obstruct
air flow over it, there should be a conspicuous warning notice —
'DO NOT COVER'.

If you have any doubts at all about any safety device, call in an expert.

TEMPERATURE CONTROL

In general, for economy and comfort all heating equipment is better
with automatic temperature control. There are one or two particular
cases where manual control has advantages but these are exceptional.

The basic item for temperature control is the thermostat. This may
be a single compact unit or it may comprise a control box with a separate
sensor.

Essentially it performs a switching action to stop heating at a preset temperature. When the temperature drops to an extent which is
usually a built-in characteristic of the unit (variable in some) heating is
restarted.

Many are built in to heaters and boilers as standard and you generally
have to accept what the manufacturer supplies. However there are cases,
especially with electric heaters, where the type of thermostatic control
can affect the performance of the unit to such an extent that it should
be taken into account in selecting the heater (see Chapter 6 — Convector
Heaters).

A more sophisticated form of control is by modulation: *ie* instead of an on/off action the heat output is reduced or increased progressively as the temperature moves away from the set point. In general this is more expensive and is not universally applicable to all types of heating. The only relatively low cost example is the thermostatic radiator valve which will be discussed further in Chapter 9. An intermediate stage is on/off control of a proportion of the heat emitters.

ROOM THERMOSTATS

There are many makers and models of room thermostats offering different detail characteristics and they will usually be selected by the supplier on the basis of price unless you take a specific interest.

The cheapest units tend to have quite a wide gap between off and on. Electronic units will control between closer limits and respond more quickly to temperature change with consequent reduction in energy use and a greater degree of comfort.

One of the main considerations is whether or not the thermostat is to be readily adjustable. In the home there is no problem and an ordinary thermostat with calibrations on an exposed dial which is free to move is completely adequate. There may be differences of opinion between family members but some compromise is usually achieved! The situation in churches and halls is totally different.

As discussed in Chapter 1 there is both a technical and a 'people' problem and this calls for much more thought.

Before choosing a thermostat the first consideration is whether the temperature can be fixed (apart from seasonal variations) once the correct setting has been established, or if, as is often the case in halls, two different temperature levels are needed for sedentary adult groups and active youth organizations.

If a fixed setting is acceptable then the requirement is for a concealed face tamper-proof thermostat. Another option is to have the adjustable thermostat itself located in a relatively inaccessible place and just a remote sensor in the occupied area.

If some variation of temperature is required this will only be within a restricted range, probably between about 14°C and 19°C (perhaps a little higher in certain special cases involving, for example, day care of the elderly — though for many years there has been a legal maximum of 19°C for public places). The lowest cost unit for this purpose is one where the settings are visible and there are maximum and minimum stops which can be set internally and require access with a special key to make changes. (An Allen key is probably the lowest practicable level of security!)

Once set the users or church officer can set the temperature normally to each stop (or intermediately) according to the use required. The users are free to vary the setting and cooperation should be sought by explaining the operation of the control and asking for the lowest practicable settings to be used. In particular it is helpful if the thermostat can be set at the appropriate level for the next organization before leaving the premises. (This will not always work!)

It will be noted that reference is made to the stops being set internally. Some of the more common thermostats designed primarily for domestic use have the stops accessible from outside. These are not recommended.

A better unit is a 'dual' room thermostat. (Some 'set-back' thermostats are suitable.) This comprises two concealed face thermostats in the same tamper-proof case. One ('high') can be set to control at a temperature of about 19°C (66°F) and the 'low' one about 4/5°C lower to suit active youth organizations. These are initial settings and should be adjusted with experience.

The thermostat normally controls at the low temperature unless a button is pressed which gives high temperature for a period determined by a timer in the unit which, in one particular make, you can pre-set at between a half hour and four hours after which control reverts to the low thermostat. As well as being time controlled it also resets to low after the heating is switched off.

When an organization requires higher temperatures, arrangements can be made for the first person arriving to press the button and by the time people are settling down most well-balanced heating systems should have raised the temperature by the few degrees needed.

There are alternative models which can be controlled by a 'high/low' switch (no timer) and by a remote time switch (which allows temperature level to be programmed in advance).

Again there is the programmable room thermostat incorporating time switch and thermostat where three or even more different temperatures can be selected. A difficulty with these is that the unit has to be located in the area to be heated. Most of those on the market, having been designed for domestic use, are not sufficiently tamper-proof to ensure that prying hands will not press one or two buttons and wreck the programme. It is bad enough to expose temperature control to the attention of users, but to give them the chance to upset times as well is to court disaster. This is an area in which development is continuing and more suitable units will certainly appear.

The calibrations of a thermostat are not always to be trusted particularly in an intermittently heated environment. Location and mounting can have effects and as a general rule for typical sedentary adult use it is advisable to start with a setting of about 19°C (66°F) and then make fine adjustments as necessary up or down with subjective experience. A thermometer can be used but at the end of the day the most reliable indicator is how people feel. The object should be to operate at the lowest setting which does not produce more than the almost inevitable isolated complaint. It has been noted elsewhere that there can be an advantage in dropping settings 2° or 3°C for a few weeks at the beginning and end of the season when there will be a tendency for air temperature to give a misleading response.

A thermograph which gives a record of temperature against time can be very useful not only in setting thermostats but also starting times. It can be particularly valuable in setting up more sophisticated controls.

Reference has been made in the chapter dealing with direct electric heating to the problems that can arise with built-in thermostats in electric convectors. If a building is currently heated with electric convectors it us useful to observe what happens by staying in the area while it is being warmed up and referring to a thermometer located centrally in the room. If the thermostats are of the wrong type they will begin to switch on and off long before an acceptable temperature is achieved.

There are many applications where manual control of radiant heaters is preferable to thermostatic control. Everyone is familiar with the instant change when an electric fire is switched off. Intermittent operation resulting from simple on/off automatic control is disturbing. In a hall, if switches are conveniently placed near heaters people tend to switch off as necessary and in practice it has been found that there is little difference in running cost compared with automatic control. In a church, someone can make an assessment of the needs appropriate to the conditions, and once the building has been given an initial full output preheat, select only those heaters necessary.

If there are multiple elements or lamps in each heater it can be useful to have a facility to select less than full heat output from the unit.

If thermostatic control is required it is advisable to use a form of control which either modulates the output of each heater or controls – say, one out of two or three elements or heat lamps – rather than switching the complete unit.

WEATHER COMPENSATORS

These are more sophisticated devices which are primarily associated with hot water systems and will be dealt with in that section.

TIME CONTROL

Time switches come in many different forms and it is important from the point of view of convenience and economy to have the right unit for the job.

Unfortunately, in many cases an installer will simply quote 'time switch' or maybe '7-day time switch' or 'programmer' without any further detail. This is completely unsatisfactory because, along with the thermostats, this is the main point of contact between the user and the heating system. It is essential that it should be capable of meeting the requirements and that the person who has to operate it is comfortable with it. At the very least you should see a comprehensive descriptive leaflet of the specific model offered. It is better still to see an instruction leaflet and even better to have 'hands-on' experience.

The most important features are the ease of checking and altering settings.

There are some basic divisions of time switches;

Simple mechanical time switches (non-digital)

(1) 24 hour with 1 or 2 pairs of on/off triggers.
(2) *24 hour with day omission (ie facility to operate the fixed programme on selected days only) and triggers as above.*
(3) 24 hour with little plastic segments that are clicked into position to give 'on' periods. (Day omission is generally not available with this type.)
(4) Seven day of the same type as (3). (This gives the facility to select different timings for each day but typically on/off times are only on even hours in two hour steps.)
(5) *Seven day with a large dial and cams which can be adjusted in length or on/off triggers.*

Of these, only (2) and (5) are of value in general church applications. The others are all unsuitable because you cannot omit days when no heating is required – (1) and (3) – or the timing is so coarse as to be wasteful (4). (There is a variation of (4) with an inner clock face which can be set more accurately but is too complicated for practical purposes.)

Of the (2) type a unit made by Sangamo has been the main standby for heating control in churches and halls for many years. A single switch will cover a church-only situation. To avoid altering the settings too often it is sometimes necessary to use a separate one for setting hall times. This is a unit that people usually understand and are happy with. There is little to be gained by changing from this to a digital unit unless the programme requirements have become more complex than it can cope with and the person responsible for operation is likely to be happy with a digital type of control.

The (5) type of time switch has not been installed for some years and existing units are tending to wear out. If the programme is such that the facility offered by this unit is needed, it is probable that an electronic seven day time switch will be the most practical option.

Electronic digital time switches

Time switches are increasingly electronic and digital. They give greater flexibility and versatility than the mechanical units but they do tend to be more difficult to programme and handle especially for anyone who has not mastered the art of programming a video recorder!

There are some which are designed for control of commercial equipment and are intended to be set once by the installing specialist and forgotten about. These are totally unsuited to church heating applications and can be a nightmare for the person who has to try to use them. Inevitably they are eventually set to some programme, usually for the worst conditions, and then never changed, with consequent waste of energy.

Even proper heating control units fall into a number of types and it is important to ensure that the one chosen has the right facilities. There are so many variations that only a selection of the more common are listed.

(1) Same programme each day with or without day omission – generally useless.
(2) Weekday/weekend – very limited application.
(3) *Seven day with each day programmable separately and a maximum of two on/off periods per day.*
(4) *Seven day with each day programmable separately and at least three on/off periods per day.*

The most useful units are (3) and (4) some of which are available as single or two channel. Two channel units are useful if you want to control say church and halls separately, always assuming that the installed systems are suitable for independent control.

Some essentially domestic time switches are relatively easy to use and have two channels marked 'central heating' and 'hot water'. Some of these can be used as two channel units but you have to make certain that you can programme the two sides completely independently (which is not always the case).

They come with all sorts of additional facilities. Most have an override button which is essential to deal with an emergency because the last thing you want is someone who is not familiar with the unit to try to get heat at an unusual time by changing the programme!

Another useful facility is an 'extend' button which allows you to extend a programmed heating period by a preset period. This also allows you to obtain the same preset period of heating at any time by pressing the button. Typically the preset period can be internally set at between one and four hours. It can of course be pressed a second time if necessary.

Some units come with illumination behind the display, but it is better to make certain that the time switch is installed at about average eye level and well illuminated.

A possibly more useful facility on some is a key which must be inserted before the programme can be changed.

There is one model which is a cross between a conventional clock and a digital which has a clock-like face on which segments corresponding to the set 'on' periods are filled in. Each day can be viewed in turn. Many people find this a very convenient and 'user friendly' compromise which is preferable to the pure 'digital'. This particular model gives a fixed 'extend' period of two hours.

Optimisers

These come as separate items, or may combine a timeswitch and the 'optimising' function with some also including a weather compensator function.

These are theoretically attractive for church and hall heating situations because they automatically take care of the fact that it takes less time to bring a building up to temperature under mild conditions than it does in the depths of winter. In principle all that is required is that you set the time switch for the worst conditions and the optimiser then delays the start by a period appropriate to prevailing conditions. Separate units are needed for church and hall because each will have quite different characteristics.

It is preferable to control from inside rather than outside temperatures with intermittently heated buildings. For example, whatever the weather it will make a difference in the church if it has been heated for a wedding on Saturday. An override facility is essential.

Experience with these has been variable. The real difficulty is in getting them properly tuned in the first place. They can only really be recommended where there is someone who is prepared to come to grips with the fairly tricky job of balancing the situation. It only takes a few failures to achieve acceptable results and the apparently attractive investment is disconnected for the sake of peace in the congregation. Nevertheless they are a method of making this necessary adjustment without being dependent on the guesswork of the person who looks after the heating.

'Self-learning' optimisers are available. These tend to be rather more expensive than can be justified for church premises, but the situation is changing and it is probable that very practical lower cost units will be on the market in the not too distant future.

Timers

These are often overlooked as a convenient method of control particularly with responsive systems. In principle you press a button or turn a knob to obtain a preset period of heating at the end of which it shuts down. If you want a longer period you press the button again. The great advantage is that you can never leave heaters on accidentally. A particularly useful application for these is electric heating in church vestibules which can be set for the period that office-bearers are normally on duty. These are sometimes available built in to electric heaters.

CASE NOTES

The majority of basic thermostats in use in church halls are set to maximum! In other words they never do anything.

A form of temperature control often associated with the high set thermostat is the open window. This gains no marks for economy.

Manual starting and stopping of heating is always suspect. Some examples:

(1) Electric heaters with no thermostatic control were found blasting away in a church vestibule on a Thursday. Someone had forgotten to switch them off on Sunday. A simple calculation demonstrated that this error had consumed 10% of the total average annual electricity of the building.

(2) Heating in a church hall switched on for the evening when the lady in charge went to collect her child from school — regardless of weather.

(3) Heating in a church switched on at either 11pm Saturday or 7pm Saturday depending on whether the beadle was going out for a drink. The early start was, of course, the drinking night! Experiment established that the correct range of starting times was from about 2am to 6am depending on weather conditions.

(9)

CONTROLS FOR HOT WATER CENTRAL HEATING

All the items mentioned in the previous chapter have their place in hot water system control but there are additional points that should be taken into account.

TEMPERATURE CONTROL

When the room thermostat signals that the set temperature has been achieved, it is important from the point of view of economy to try to prevent the boiler from firing just to keep itself warm.

(NOTE: Reference will be made to a 'single' boiler. It should be understood that this can comprise two or even more boilers connected as modules. For all practical purposes these constitute a single boiler for general control. See Chapter 5 for more about boilers.)

(1) With a single boiler serving a single heated zone there is no problem — operation of the room thermostat should stop the boiler. With most modern installations the pump will continue to 'run-on' for about five minutes to dissipate heat from the boiler. If this facility is not already built into the installation then it is a good idea to add it or alternatively connect the room thermostat to control the boiler leaving the pump running. It is bad practice to have the thermostat controlling the pump while leaving the boiler to carry on firing at will. This costs energy and money and could shorten the life of some low water content modern boilers.

(2) For a single boiler serving a church and a hall with manual valves controlling the two zones and with a single pump, the following is a convenient arrangement.

Connect room thermostats installed in the church and in the hall through a selector switch ('church' and 'hall') linked to control the boiler leaving the pump running (or on 'run-on'). The selector switch is used to select whether control is by the church thermostat or the hall one. With this arrangement and the switch set to 'hall', the boiler will be shut off when the hall does not require heat.

This has the obvious shortcoming in that there is no control over temperature in the hall when the church is being heated. However, unless there is a new and generously sized heating installation in the hall, this is unlikely to cause too much of a problem and it will, even then, probably only occur on an occasional Sunday morning. Turning off a few radiators or a partial closing of a manual valve on the hall circuit should, with a little experience, give a reasonable balance. The great merit of this arrangement is that, apart from that specific situation, it does give a very good, energy efficient, control system at extremely low capital cost.

(3) If there are separate pumps for the church and hall this gives the possibility in some cases of controlling the pumps by the thermostats, but it will be more economical to adopt the same arrangement as described in paragraph (2) for a single pump. Most modern boilers *must* have continuous pumped circulation during firing and for a run-on period of some minutes after. This is a point which should be checked when a new boiler has been installed.

If the pumps are controlled by separate time switches it is an easy matter to have automatic selection of which room thermostat is in control by means of a relay in the church pump circuit.

(4) The next possibility is a single boiler with single or multiple pumps and motorized valves controlling, say, the church and hall circuits. When designed in this way there ought to be a circuit which is not controlled by valve, *eg* toilets and entrance which will absorb some of the excess heat and power of the pump when all valves are closed.

Provided that this is the case then each valve may be controlled by the corresponding thermostat. Motorized valves are generally fitted with auxiliary switches and it is not difficult to arrange that when there is no demand from heat from any controlled zone the boiler is shut down.

If the valves are not fitted with auxiliary switches the same result can be achieved with relays.

From the above it will be appreciated that there is a considerable simplification of controls when one boiler is used for the church and one for the halls as discussed in Chapter 5. In this situation paragraph (1) above is applicable.

With older systems which have substantial water content it is practicable to switch off heating some time before the end of the period of occupation. To a lesser extent this is also true of more modern systems. To avoid waste, heating should always be switched off before doors are opened at the end of occupation.

WEATHER COMPENSATOR

It is good practice to vary boiler operating temperature according to external conditions. With gas boilers it can be varied from about 80°C in mid-winter to about 60°C at the beginning and end of the season. The reduction in emission of heat from the system at the lower temperature is about 40%. In the case of oil-fired boilers they should not be set below about 65°C to avoid corrosion resulting from the return water temperature dropping below the dew point. There is usually no difficulty in making this adjustment manually as the season progresses but it is not really practicable to adjust manually on a day-to-day basis. A weather compensator does this constantly and automatically.

This form of temperature control can be useful in halls generally and in churches which have heating by pipe coils under pews or by modern low water content radiator systems. It is not suitable for use with hot water fan convectors which should normally be run at full boiler temperature. It can be difficult to assess the financial benefit as this depends very much on how thoughtfully the system was operated before the addition of the compensator.

Only weather compensators, which have an internal sensor as well as an outside one and a facility to maintain the boiler operating temperature at maximum while raising the room temperature to the set figure before beginning to control, should be used, especially in churches. In the absence of this facility it can be difficult to be certain that the building is fully heated as required. This also makes for economic operation. It is also desirable that the compensator should incorporate a device for restricting boiler firing cycles.

With oil-fired boilers the practice has been to use 3-port mixing valves to vary circulating water temperature while keeping the boiler set at near maximum. This was done to avoid corrosion. It is more expensive than direct boiler temperature control. Some newer oil fired boilers are said to be suitable for direct control but this should be verified from maker's documents.

It will be apparent that it may not be all that easy to apply this equipment in cases where there is a single boiler serving both church and hall unless each system has a separate mixing valve controlled by a separate compensator.

THERMOSTATIC RADIATOR VALVES

While these are a very useful device in domestic situations they have to be used with some thought in church and hall buildings.

The first and most important point is that with one or two exceptions the typical domestic type is simply not robust enough to stand up to the harsh environment of a church hall! Within a year it can be expected that about 50% of the lighter models will be ineffective and the radiators will be operating at full temperature.

To be worth fitting they must be of the commercial type with 'vandal-proof' stops that can be preset to limit the upper setting at least (to about the mid position). The lower setting will depend on whether you need the facility to shut off completely or simply have a low setting for certain organizations.

In general, it will be found that for halls a room thermostat system which exercises control over the boiler is a better investment (see above). It will probably cost considerably less than a set of good quality TRVs and will operate the boiler with significantly better fuel economy.

The most useful application is in rooms and offices.

RADIATOR SURFACE TEMPERATURE

With none of the above controls is there any assurance that the radiators may not sometimes heat up to near boiler maximum temperature.

In an area where elderly infirm or very young children may come in contact with the radiators it is better not to depend on controls. (See Chapter 10 – Safety.)

FROST PROTECTION

Consideration should always be given to the installation of an automatic frost protection system. This could consist of a single froststat located at the foot of an exposed window in a part of the building with heating installed and connected to bypass the time switch. Boiler(s), pump(s) and motorised valve(s) should all be activated. The froststat should be set at about $+3°C$ to $+5°C$. With this arrangement the system will shut down when the inside temperature rises a few degrees.

If the boiler house is liable to be the coldest area it is advisable to fit a second unit in it, connected so that if either of the froststats calls for heat the system will operate and continue till both are satisfied.

This is a very simple arrangement which allows you to set a minimum temperature for the building which could be slightly higher than the above if you wished, provided that you remember that each degree higher will significantly increase fuel costs.

To place a single froststat in the boiler house only is risky because temperature in the boiler house can rise quite quickly once the boiler starts and may cut out the boiler before there has been a significant rise in the temperature throughout the system.

A complete alternative is an outside froststat connected to control the pumps. A second frostat is installed in a return pipe (or strapped to it) and connected to control the boiler. The external unit should be set to operate at about $+3°C$. The inside unit could be set at $+10°C$, or higher if some little heat is wanted in the building under such circumstances to protect other water services.

A check should be carried out annually to ensure that the system is operational and that a satisfactory compromise is being maintained between protection and economy. In particular, be aware of heating having been on when neither time control nor conditions appear to call for it and, on the other hand, no hint of heat when a little would have been expected.

An unsatisfactory and potentially very wasteful system is to have an external froststat connected to control the boiler and pump. With this arrangement there is nothing to stop the boiler firing until the building is fully heated and then it will carry on as necessary to maintain full heat until the outside temperature rises. These are rarely found now but in a cold winter have been known to waste as much fuel in a few weeks as should have heated the church for the whole year.

A small tubular heater should be installed adjacent to the expansion tank if it is in a cold location which does not benefit from the main frost protection system. It should be controlled by a local froststat set at about 5°C.

CASE NOTE

Beware of the 'Black Box' (it comes with a variety of names) which is '. . . simply installed in the boiler thermostat circuit and is guaranteed to save 25% by preventing the boiler firing unnecessarily'. To cut a long story short, it is a waste of money and you will be lucky to get a refund. These are rarely offered by reputable heating engineers.

(10)

HEATING DESIGN AND SAFETY

This chapter takes an overall look at the heating of churches and halls from the point of view of determining the main factors involved when a full replacement of heating is being considered. Much of the content is also relevant for partial replacement or upgrading.

While it may seem to be easy to go out to the electricity and gas supply companies and some heating and electrical contractors asking for proposals and prices for a variety of schemes, it is often difficult to make a decision because the proposals will almost certainly be impossible to compare properly without some understanding and consideration of factors other than simply price.

A much better approach is to employ a professional consulting engineer experienced in church work. They are not very plentiful but it should be possible to trace one through your own or another church organization. It need not cost a large fee if you limit the involvement to those areas where independence and experience are of most importance. Typically:

(1) An initial survey and report with options, recommendations and budget figures.
(2) A meeting to discuss and decide.
(3) Preparation of a brief specification setting out technical require-ments for equipment and controls plus essential contract conditions. (You can then obtain quotations from selected competent contractors, preferably known, at least by reputation, to you or the consultant.)
(4) Assessment of quotations and recommendation to you.
(5) (Optional) Meeting on site between consultant and contractor.

(6) (Optional) Visit to site by consultant during installation.

(7) Final check at time of commissioning.

This will cost much less than a full consulting engineering procedure, but do discuss fees before you start. The responsibility for the design will lie with the consultant and the responsibility for the installation with the contractor.

The rest of this chapter may read like a DIY Guide but that is not the intention. The primary object is to give an understanding of what has to be considered and give some rule of thumb guidance to help you check information provided. It should also be of help if you decide to go directly to supply companies and contractors and alert you to things to look out for if you follow that approach.

Some points made elsewhere are summarized here but to minimize repetition the reader is asked to refer also to the appropriate chapters.

HEAT REQUIREMENT

One of the first points to consider is how much heat is needed. (NOTE: $1kW = 3414Btu/hr$.)

For a continuously or regularly heated building the recognized method is to calculate the steady state heat loss through the fabric under defined conditions of external and internal temperature.

To calculate this you determine the areas of wall (excluding windows), windows, roof and floor and also calculate the volume.

With a knowledge of the construction of the various parts you then apply a factor known as the U-value which is a measure of heat loss in watts per square meter per degree Celsius differential inside to out. (Typically about 20°C for church buildings.) This gives a heat loss through each component of the fabric under stable conditions of slight frost. (It is worth bearing in mind that to design for extremes of cold would be prohibitively expensive and that this is a practical compromise which will inevitably be revealed as inadequate under extreme conditions!)

The volume is used to calculate the heat loss due to air change and is based on an assumed number of air changes per hour. (In many cases this is the least determinate part of the calculation.)

Given a set of tables, the calculation of total heat loss is not usually too difficult provided that you know the construction of the building and have details of any insulation added.

Modern buildings have to be constructed to minimum insulation standards. Drawings and specifications will generally be available. Failing this the basic Building Regulation standard appropriate to the date of design can be assumed.

Computer programmes are available which make short work of the heat loss calculation once you have done the measuring and checked construction details. Even before the days of computers there were various manual slide-rule type calculators available.

For an intermittently heated building such as a church heated once or even a few days a week, the more technically correct method is to calculate all the exposed areas of fabric within the building and then apply factors representing the rate of absorption ('admittance') of heat by these surfaces.

These are different factors and the calculation is substantially more complex because, for example, the surface area of galleries and stone pillars among other items need to be taken into account.

The difficulty with all of these is that it takes time and practice to become familiar with what is involved and they are not really suitable for the person who is faced with a once-in-a-lifetime calculation.

Unfortunately, the proper calculation is also time consuming for the tenderer. Time costs money, especially when he knows that he probably has no better than a one in three or four chance of getting a contract, and short cuts are taken.

One such technique is to look at the size of the boiler installed, make some assumptions about boiler margins, add a bit on and hope for the best. Another short cut is to measure up the existing system, calculate its emission and assume that it is about 75% of what is needed for present standards.

The writer came across a very old treatise on church heating which included a graph relating church volume to required heat input. This

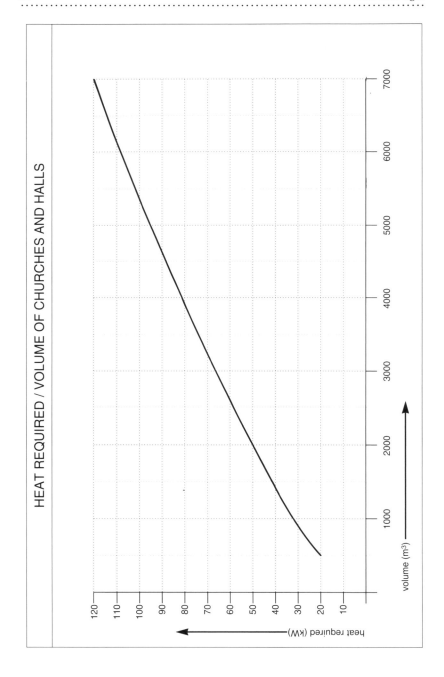

HEAT REQUIRED / VOLUME OF CHURCHES AND HALLS

was checked against calculated figures for many buildings and also against actual installations, thermograph (*ie* temperature/time) records, and user's comments on the quality of heating achieved.

It was found, as might be expected, that the line given in the old chart gave a heat input less than was needed to give today's standards in reasonably short preheat periods. It was, however, remarkably consistent over a very wide range of buildings so the curve was adjusted to bring it up to date for the typical stone or brick building of 'pre-insulation' days — *ie* something like 95% of all church buildings. It is not applicable to modern fully insulated buildings.

The revised chart has been used regularly as a spot check method and while it cannot be 100% accurate it is much more so than many contractors' calculations.

The modified graph is reproduced here so that anyone who can calculate the volume of the heated building can make a quick check on about how much heating is needed. Points to bear in mind are that it will give a slightly low reading (up to 10%) for a church with bare stone walls or in a very exposed situation. It will give a slightly high reading (again up to about 10%) for halls which are heated daily, increasing to about 15% if the loft is also fully insulated). Rooms below the minimum on the chart will generally have rather lower ceilings, and a rule of thumb is that the radiator emission should certainly be no less than 100 watts per square metre of floor area, and for a high ceiling or an intermittent heating situation a figure of 130/150 watts per square metre would be better.

(NOTE: The most difficult part of the calculation of the volume of the church is the determination of inaccessible heights. If you cannot come by the appropriate equipment then the most useful tip is probably to stand either in the gallery or the pulpit and use a ruler at arm's length to compare measured horizontal distances with verticals at the far end of the building. Then get someone else to assess the heights independently — and discuss the differences! Do *not* use traditionally quoted heights without checking.)

Where boilers are involved, the question of the margin over the installed heating is discussed in Chapter 5.

Almost unbelievable variations can occur in installations offered by contractors. The real danger is that it is often found that the lowest price is achieved by offering an undersized installation. Unless some form of check is carried out, the congregation can find that they have spent a substantial sum on a heating system that is inadequate.

This usually leads to a couple of winters of argument and general discontent followed by action involving the installation of additional heating. If a boiler was involved it is probably too small to carry additional radiators and resort has to be made to some alternative form of heating to make up the discrepancy. The end result can be a bit of a mess probably costing more than an alternative correctly sized proposal turned down originally because of price.

QUOTATIONS

Quotations for 'a heating system' should never be given any consideration unless they specify one or two things. Preferably there should be a description and rated output of each heat emitter in each separate heated area. Alternatively a contractor may guarantee achievable internal temperature with an acceptable stated external temperature (usually $-1°C$).

The latter is satisfactory up to a point, but if new heating is installed during the summer it may well be January or February before conditions arise which show up deficiencies, and unless it has been agreed prior to contract that some of the total payment will be retained pending such practical testing there may be little real comeback. Given the rated output figures and the approximate heat requirement from the graph it is possible to make a check before placing an order.

Another advantage in being given heat emitter output is that it facilitates comparison between different proposals for different types of system which can be compared on a 'cost per kW of installed heating' basis: (In central heating, the installed heating is the sum of the emitter outputs – and not the boiler size – which normally must be more. See Chapter 5).

Theoretically, systems based on radiant heating are intended to heat the individual and not the building and therefore it is sometimes argued that less heating is needed. In practice, if the whole building is to be heated there is generally not a lot of difference in the total heat requirement whatever the system. Only in buildings which are very high in relation to floor area will the correct result for radiant heaters be markedly less than the graph will give. (In this case a rule of thumb for heating the complete floor area is 200 to 240 watts per square metre.)

Radiant heaters may be used locally to heat the front of a church or a side chapel, but to do this with any degree of satisfaction the intensity of heating over that area must be substantially greater – at least 50% – than for a whole building situation, and even then the comfort level will probably only be acceptable for short services.

The other type of heating which requires a larger heat input than will be derived by this method is the direct gas fired warm air system, *ie* the system which draws air from outside, heats the air by burning gas in it and blows it into the building creating a small pressure which forces warm air out through ventilators or gaps in the fabric. In this case the heat loss due to air change is much higher than other methods of heating and consequently the heaters are often two or more times more powerful than the graph will show. (NOTE: This must not be interpreted as indicating low overall efficiency, because among other factors the absence of any heat loss at the burner and the relatively small amount of heat put into the fabric makes this a particularly efficient form of heating.)

Because the effectiveness of this type of heating is dependent on leakage which may be difficult to identify positively, it is important to ensure that the contractor undertakes or specifies any sealing work required on the building in advance so that the full cost can be determined before placing an order. This should not be left as an open ended liability for the buyer.

TYPE OF HEATING

If a completely new heating system is being considered there are many factors which need to be taken into account.

Energy source

The first thought will probably be to continue with the existing energy source, unless natural gas has become available when it will almost certainly be considered as an alternative.

In general, gas and electricity tend to be the most favoured provided that the necessary supply is available. (You may find that you have a choice of suppliers.)

However, oil has for many years been the cheapest practical form of energy for church and hall heating provided that the user conscientiously kept an eye on the price being charged and changed suppliers (or threatened to do so) when the price crept up. There are many reasons why it should continue to be the cheapest, but this is not a subject on which anyone is likely to give guarantees since there are many pressures at play in addition to market forces. (In some areas congregations have combined to negotiate an annual contract.)

LPG (Liquified Petroleum Gas) is derived from oil and is delivered by bottle or into a pressurized tank. It is generally the most expensive form of energy for heating. For some time it has been around 80 to 100% dearer than oil depending on the size of deliveries.

In practical situations an electric boiler will always cost more to run than an oil or mains gas-fired boiler. There are virtually no circumstances in which an electric boiler has any advantage over electricity used directly in local heaters.

Electricity is an acceptable energy source provided that you do not foresee using much during mornings and afternoons Monday to Friday. This allows use of an Evening and Weekend tariff which gives a favourable rate at other times and is offered by most supply companies. Some 'off-peak' tariffs may be suitable (see Chapter 11).

Environmental matters

If the potential for pollution is to be taken into account this can be more difficult than might be expected. On the face of it, electricity is the cleanest and least polluting, but if generated in a thermal (coal, oil or gas) station less than 30% of the energy in the primary fuel is delivered to your building as useful heat, the balance being lost in generation and distribution. In contrast, at least 60% and possibly over 70% of the energy in the fuel burnt in a boiler on site is delivered into the building. With the most efficient direct gas heaters the figure is even better.

If the electricity is generated by a nuclear station then there *should be* virtually no direct pollution but you have to make up your own mind about the other consequences of using nuclear power!

If the electricity is generated by a water or wind scheme then you are really doing your bit because there is no pollution – but if you are taking your supply from the mains you have no control over how it is generated. So by using electricity your action may range from the best possible to the worst possible from the point of view of resources and pollution!

Gas is less of a pollutant than either oil or coal.

Comfort rating

As a broad generalization there tends to be a higher level of user satisfaction with hot water central heating than with direct forms of heating. Direct heating may cost less to run (except electric heating at expensive times) but most of them have limitations which need to be taken into account.

One of the best alternatives to central heating is the balanced flue gas convector. This can be time and temperature controlled conveniently and gives a high degree of convected heat which people tend to prefer. Unfortunately whereas with a central heating system you may find that you have only to replace the boiler after about 20 years, you may well find that you are faced with replacing all gas convectors after about the same period. This will cost a great deal more than a boiler and cancel out much of the benefit of the low running cost.

Servicing costs

Servicing is another factor which reduces the economic advantage of individual gas heaters. With central heating most of the installation except the boiler will work with little attention for many years, whereas each direct gas heater ought to have annual servicing to maintain performance and safety standards.

Servicing is a point in favour of electric heaters as generally nothing requires regular attention. Elements or lamps can last many years though reflectors of radiant heaters may need attention from time to time. Fan heaters require cleaning but if you refer to the section dealing with electric heating these are generally not recommended for other reasons (Chapter 6).

Controls

The importance of simple controls in church buildings is often overlooked. It is all too easy to become carried away with the really ingenious equipment that is increasingly available.

Unfortunately, controls do go wrong and unless you understand exactly what they are meant to do it is difficult for the layman to recognize where the problem lies. This means calling in an expensive expert.

While there are undoubtedly benefits in efficiency to be made with sophisticated controls, these do cost quite a lost of money and the savings will only be made if they are regularly checked and adjusted and used with understanding.

It is with central heating in particular that there is a temptation to add to controls. This is one of the several advantages in having separate boilers for the church and halls as discussed in Chapter 5.

Appearance

This is necessarily a very subjective issue which will rate more highly in some churches than others. How does it rate in a case where a congregation has very little money and the choice may lie between heating of some sort (even with some visual impact) and closing the doors permanently?

In general, heating should be as inconspicuous as possible and this was certainly the case where in Victorian times hot water pipes in a duct under the aisles was often specified. Unfortunately, while this was a perfect solution for the architect and was a satisfactory method of heating, given enough pipes and extended heating periods, it was not an efficient arrangement for an intermittently heated church.

Another type of heating used in more modern churches has been electrical and hot water underfloor heating. While some recent developments suggest that this may become more economical in certain cases — generally new buildings, it is not a method of heating which should be considered as replacement heating.

One of the best combinations of inconspicuousness and effectiveness is hot water pipes under pews. Hot water fan convectors can also be relatively easily concealed or disguised.

At the other extreme are radiant heaters and these are all necessarily conspicuous because there has to be a direct line of slight between the heater and the object heated. The most conspicuous are radiant tube gas heaters and radiant quartz heaters. These are probably the most difficult on which to make decisions because they both give relatively low capital outlay and running costs, even if they do not give the ultimate in comfort.

An item which is sometimes advanced as an energy saving device, and may have considerable visual impact, is the ceiling fan. With most forms of heating the temperature difference found in church buildings is very much less than that suggested in the advertising material for fans and consequently the potential for gaining comfort or saving energy is less than might be expected. Before considering the installation of fans it is recommended that temperature readings should be taken at floor level and high level, with the church or hall fully heated but empty, and preferably also during occupation. A pair of thermographs can be used. These must be calibrated together for temperature, one suspended at high level and the other placed on a seat. Maximum/minimum thermometers are a simpler device and more readily available, but can only give spot checks and consequently more tests will be needed. With these, it is again best to use two. They should be checked by leaving for a time at the same level and then one transferred to the highest practical level for long enough to reach stability – say about 10 minutes – and then lowered. In general terms, if differences are less than 5°C it will not be worth considering fans. If consistently more then it is probably worth going on to prepare a design and assess visual factors.

Sound

It is important that the heating system should not make noise at an intrusive level. Very low levels of noise are lost in an occupied church but it does not need much to be noticeable. Clicks and start/stop noises tend to be more distracting than a continuous low level of noise. Some gas heaters of various types tend to be rather noisy when starting under thermostatic control. A modulating control is to be preferred.

The noisiest items likely to be encountered are electric fan heaters (see Chapter 6).

Unless care is taken at the design stage there can be problems with warm air systems and radiant gas tubes which have not been properly silenced. It is important that controls ensure that hot water fan convectors cannot operate above low speed during a service.

There are circumstances when it is important to consider the sound from a boiler. This can arise when a new boiler is being installed in a different location usually when an underground boiler house is being abandoned. If the new location is near the church or halls it is possible that a pressure jet oil burner or a blown gas burner may make enough noise to be a nuisance. As a generalization blown gas burners tend to be noisier than oil burners. Atmospheric type gas burners make very little noise and can be used in most situations.

SAFETY

This is a more difficult field than might be expected. The main problem is that situations which have been acceptable for decades can suddenly be reclassified as dangerous.

Consultants and contractors will be aware of their own responsibilities, but it is essential that those responsible for buildings open to the public should make themselves aware of their own position. (See Bibliography.)

From the point of view of fire safety of the buildings it is worth remembering that central heating has the advantage of avoiding the need for distribution of electricity or gas to points all over the buildings. Electricity will of course be in most areas anyway but electric heating does involve a separate additional set of usually well loaded cables and outlets that are often in use when the building is empty. With central heating the combustion all takes place in the boiler with electricity only being required for controls or possibly fans.

Warm air heating by one or two large central units also restricts the distribution of gas.

A factor which is becoming increasingly important is the surface temperature of the heat emitter particularly where this is in a position where it can be touched by children or the elderly.

At present this is most likely to be of concern in a hall or rooms which is used for a creche or play group. In such an area the best practice would be to provide guards over any heat emitters where the surface temperature can be too high. In general terms this will apply to most electric convectors (including some which are claimed to have low surface temperature) to balanced flue gas convectors, *and* to conventional central heating radiators.

Where the emitter incorporates a fan (*ie* hot water fan convectors and fan assisted balanced flue gas convectors) it will often be the case that this will keep the temperature down to a satisfactory level.

Low surface temperature central heating radiators are available. These operate with water at normal temperature but are so designed that exposed surfaces are air cooled to an acceptable extent (43°C). They are generally larger and more expensive than conventional radiators. They also have a lower 'comfort rating' because of the reduced direct heat radiation (see Chapter 1 – People Heating).

It is of course possible to reduce the surface temperature of ordinary radiators to some extent by dropping the boiler temperature. This however also reduces the heat emitted and typically a drop in boiler temperature from about 80°C to 60°C (roughly from about maximum to minimum setting on a boiler thermostat) will reduce effective heating by about 40%, so that if the installation is designed on a conventional basis it will not be possible to heat the building properly in cold weather.

The best answer, and in many cases the only practical one, is to use the existing heaters at normal temperature and add wire guards. These are usually available locally or advertised in church/school equipment magazines. They are generally available with a coated finish which makes them more acceptable.

Pipes which are exposed will also need covering. Small bore connecting pipes can be covered with conventional insulation with a protective surface. Pipes of 50mm or more in diameter probably make a significant contribution to the heat input and should be covered with wire guards or boxed in with substantial gaps (not less than 25mm at floor level on the vertical face and against the wall on the top face).

Where pews are against the wall and cast-iron pipes are replaced with radiators people will be much more likely to make contact. This is because (a) the tops of the radiators will be near the level of the pew and (b) a leg can be in contact with a large flat surface instead of the more or less point contact with a pipe. A neat wooden barrier will often be the best solution. It is important not to have any obstruction above the radiators as it is essential to have free air flow and this may already be partly restricted by the pew seats.

Guards

It is essential that all guards (including those on pipes) should be designed and installed so that they can be readily opened or removed to allow for removal or the dirt and debris that will inevitably accumulate.

(11)

GENERAL PURPOSE ELECTRICITY AND ELECTRICITY TARIFFS

This chapter is primarily intended to cover electricity use for purposes *other than main heating* but it will be necessary to take the latter into account when considering tariffs. The correct selection of tariff can be a significant factor in costs. If main heating is NOT by electricity it is often possible to save as much as 25% by changing from a General tariff to an 'Evening and Weekend' tariff.

In cost terms electricity is a substantial factor in the total energy bill of most congregations even where it is not used for main heating. The amount of energy may be relatively small, but with standing charges and (in some cases) premium rates for the first few hundred units each period general electricity tariffs tend to make the first two or three thousand units per annum average out at very high rates compared with other energy sources.

There are two approaches to keeping down costs. One is to minimize electricity use and the other is to make certain you are on the most suitable tariffs.

It is very difficult to analyse general (as distinct from main heating) electricity use from an inspection of the buildings and installation as it is only possible to take note of the type of lighting and the extent of electricity provision for portable heaters, domestic hot water and general kitchen use.

Beyond this, an analysis of consumption based on frequent (once or twice a day) meter readings and observations over a week or two is generally necessary. A parallel record of the use being made of the buildings should be kept.

These two sets of information will help the observer to analyse the position and identify the high points of usage for possible further action.

Another item to look out for is consumption which continues when the buildings are not in use and when all electricity is believed to be off.

ECONOMIES

The most common places to look for economy are –

Church lighting

This is usually on the relatively inefficient conventional tungsten lamp. This is not all that important if lighting is used only during a service or two on Sundays. The time required for the service is short but – is *full* lighting on for longer than really necessary before and after services? Is *full* lighting used for extended periods at high rates during the week for cleaning? If the church is open for visitors during the day, is it possible to establish a minimum practicable level of lighting – preferably based on carefully placed, more efficient lamps?

Other internal lighting

Lighting in other buildings is usually based on fluorescent or other more efficient lamps. Again, are lights on longer than necessary? Are there areas where controls could be used to switch on automatically when a person enters the area and switch off after they leave? If tungsten lights are still used in regularly lighted areas, consider changing to compact fluorescents. In some cases it is simply a matter of buying and putting in a new bulb. These are relatively very expensive to buy but soon pay for themselves where lighting has to be on for long periods.

Outside lighting

Lighting on approaches and around buildings for security and safety can use a lot of electricity. Some of these lights may need to be on all evening but others may be suitable for automatic control using local movement sensors. Timing should be checked. Outside lights are often set for mid-winter conditions and left at that as daylight extends. Automatically variable time switches are available or the combination of a low light sensor to switch on and a time switch to switch off after normal closing time may help.

More information about the various types of lamp and their application will be found in Chapter 13 and 14.

Domestic hot water

This is frequently supplied from a substantial tank heated with an electric immersor. Provided that the tank is well-lagged this is not too extravagant for occasions when a lot of hot water is needed. That, however, is not the normal situation found in church premises. For most purposes local small five or ten litre heaters or instant heaters will be much more economical. In any case they should be switched off when not required. If there is a heavy and continuous demand and gas is available it may pay to install a multi-point gas heater or a cylinder heated normally from the central heating boiler (gas or oil) with an immersor for summer back-up. Reference has been made in Chapter 5 to the use of combi boilers in suitable situations.

Local electric heaters

Portable electric heaters or fixed heaters may be used in rooms when main heating is not installed or as an alternative to main heating for small meetings. This is usually fairly easily watched. The important actions are to use thermostats and to switch off when finished.

A specific case, which is not uncommon, is a room occupied by a church secretary most mornings and heated by electricity because main heating is not on. This can add up to a considerable annual consumption and this may be identified in the check suggested below. In such a case it can be useful to install a small storage heater controlled by a plug-in time switch to take its charge during the night. This will provide a base heat which can be topped up as necessary by a thermostatically controlled convector when the room is in use. This shift of demand may be sufficient to change the balance of use in favour of the 'Evening and Weekend' tariff and allow most consumption at a lower rate. (NOTE: it will NOT pay to put in a storage heater AND stay on General tariff.)

Other items

Items which have been found to use electricity continuously and often without the knowledge of those responsible are—

Heaters and humidifiers within the organ casing. If on 'Evening and Weekend' tariff, these can often be timed to operate at low rate times only without any significant disadvantage.

Heaters under a water tank in a loft and frost protection heaters in toilets. These should be controlled by local froststats.

TARIFFS

It is difficult to write about tariffs in general terms and impossible to predict future developments so that the main point is to be aware of the alternative tariffs available and review the position from time to time – say annually or whenever a revision of rates takes place.

At the time of writing there are three main tariffs which are of interest to church congregations. In addition, Catering tariff may be applicable in a limited number of cases.

(1) The basic general commercial tariff is usually NOT the best for church premises unless:

(a) operated in conjunction with main heating on an off-peak tariff where the hours of availability are acceptable and rates are at least as favourable as 'Evening and Weekend' tariffs referred to below,

(b) or where consumption is very small, such as in a small country church with no hall attached and where the heating is by some means other than electricity,

(c) or where there is very heavy use of the premises during mornings and afternoons Monday to Friday so that the balance of consumption is unsuitable for the 'Evening and Weekend' tariff (see below).

(2) Off-peak or Economy tariffs. Some off-peak tariffs may be available at suitable times but the majority are not sufficiently flexible. Economy tariffs are only suitable in quite exceptional circumstances because unlike most off-peak tariffs they do not give extended hours at weekends.

(3) 'Evening and Weekend' tariffs are usually the most suitable for church premises where main heating is not by electricity. If main heating is by electricity the availability of a supply at all times of this type of tariff will often make it more attractive than the combination of general and off-peak even if costs are increased a little. The general principle is that all electricity used in the evenings and at all times during weekends for any purpose is at a relatively low rate, with a slightly higher rate than the general tariff during the day Monday to Friday. The usual practice is that all consumption must be on this tariff (except for Catering).

(4) 'Catering' tariff may be of use where a congregation have an all-electric kitchen and make extensive use of the facility – say with a daily coffee shop or lunch club. Provided that it is practicable to arrange for all catering electricity to be metered separately (probably with some capital outlay) this can make a useful saving.

In most cases where main heating is NOT by electricity and the church is used mainly on Sundays with the hall principally in use in the evenings, it will pay to change to an 'Evening and Weekend' tariff. In other cases, or if there is doubt, a simple check can be made.

(1) Obtain a current tariff leaflet to give rates and times.

(2) Take meter readings at appropriate times each day over a couple of typical winter weeks. These will allow you to calculate the quantity of electricity used at high and low rates.

(3) Calculate the cost over a year on both the existing tariff and the Evening and Weekend tariff.

(NOTE: In most cases it is possible to change back to a general tariff after a year if experience shows that a mistake has been made. However, it will not be possible to revert back to a discontinued off-peak tariff.)

ACCOUNTS

It is important to check all estimated accounts especially if the tariff includes a number of premium rate units for each billing period. If you do not check the readings you may find that, especially during summer months, you will be billed with more units at the premium rate than you should be. For the same reason, with tariffs of this type it is not a good idea to have a monthly billing based on an annual meter reading which will probably be based on the assumption that you use the maximum number of premium rate units every period. For most churches this is not the case during the summer.

(12)
TARGETING AND MONITORING

Are we using too much energy?
How do we establish a target figure to check how we are performing?
We are thinking about a new heating system. How are the different options likely to compare in running costs?

This is a key part of the work of the Energy Officer. At first sight the following may look daunting, but it requires no more than one or two evenings to take measurements, collect information about the pattern of use of the buildings and make the calculations.

There is an immediate benefit in that the target figures can be checked against your recent consumption (taking care to work from actual and not estimated meter readings) to see how you have been performing. There may be an indication that you are fairly close, or the figures may be such as to set alarm bells ringing and indicate a need for a thorough investigation.

Once the targets have been established, an hour a month will be sufficient to monitor the situation. Heating and lighting consumption and costs will be under control. You can arrange for regular and meaningful reports to the management body of the congregation and be in a position to check the effects of changes designed to reduce consumption. If something has gone wrong and energy use has risen you will know about it within a month, instead of having to wait for months for a bill based on a meter reading.

It is not practicable to compare similar or even identical church buildings without going into considerable detail because they are almost certainly used in different ways.

Figures have been published by some bodies for typical annual consumption for church buildings, usually related to floor area. Those examined have been found to be over-simplified and liable to very large inaccuracies.

The method outlined below was developed for *Make the Most of It* some 12 years ago. There have been revisions since then. For very little effort it provides a means of determining a rough target for checking your own performance. You can then try to beat the target or your own best performance.

These calculations do not have any scientific basis. They were arrived at by taking a selection of the more efficient examples encountered in early energy surveys, adjusting these figures for perceived further improvements and working backwards to find the simplest possible method of relating building size and usage to energy use. It was found that there was a reasonably good relationship between what is here termed the 'Weekly Heated Volume' (WHV) and energy use for heating. Experience has led to some factors being modified but the calculation remains essentially the same as the original. Derived targets have been tested against figures obtained in many other surveys and have proved a reliable indicator.

A similar exercise was carried out for electricity other than main heating. The relationship here was between 'Weekly Used Area' (WUA) and consumption. This is a less consistent relationship than the calculation for main heating as there can be considerable variations depending on many different circumstances. It is, however significantly better than nothing and if calculations show that you are using much more than the target suggested, then further investigation will be well justified.

The figures should be viewed as being average for conditions in Scotland. They will tend to under-estimate for a highland glen and over-estimate for a sheltered corner in the south-west. There are cold winters and mild winters and these will also influence the actual figures. So long as this is recognized and it is accepted that the figures do not pretend to be more than a basic guide, you will find them useful.

(NOTE: 'Degree Day Analysis' is a technique which can be used to take weather variations into account for region to region and year to year comparisons. The Energy Efficiency Office will provide data and advice on use on request – see Bibliography. It can be taken that figures derived from the calculations in this chapter relate to an area with an annual degree day figure of about 2750 using a base temperature of 15.5°C.)

The calculations are applicable to typical church buildings with or without halls. It does not really matter if they are Victorian stone or 20th century brick. They are, however, not appropriate to modern insulated buildings, but these were very few at the time of writing and can be reasonably assumed to be efficient in most respects in order to comply with Building Regulations. As a rule of thumb, if the actual figures for heating such a building are more than half the target calculated by this method, there is something seriously wrong. For general purpose electricity, the calculated target should be met with ease.

It is important to view the results in the correct perspective. It is possible that with all practicable economies having been made, a basic fault such as a grossly oversized boiler may make it impossible to reach the target without substantial capital expenditure.

It is always possible to achieve low consumption figures by freezing the users. This is not recommended. Generally, if the actual figures are better than the target by more than about 20% this is usually found to be the case!

The basic information required for assessment is the floor area (m^2) and volume (m^3) of the church and of each hall or larger meeting room, together with information about the typical pattern of use during the heating season (see note in Chapter 10 on estimating heights).

Provision for typical 'extra' weekday heatings for weddings and funerals, Easter and Christmas is built-in at a level of about 10/12 a year. So are special hall heatings at a level of about once a month to take care of coffee mornings and so on. If there are more like 25 such heatings per year add 0.5 to both 'heating' and 'use' factors discussed below.

In calculating areas and volumes, all 'service' areas should be omitted, *eg* vestry, small meeting rooms (less than about 30m^2), kitchen, toilets, passages, *etc*. Include the church vestibule with the church if it is inside the main block of the building. Include the hall platform with the hall concerned.

Prepare a table as follows for each hall or larger meeting room. It will probably not be necessary to make up a table for the church.

Mark 'X' against each morning, afternoon, and evening session where the hall is used and heated.

Mark 'O' against each session where the hall is used without being heated (*eg* badminton period following another organization with heating switched off).

Heating Factor = 1.0 for each day on which the hall is heated + 0.2 for each additional heating session on the same day.

(NOTE: If heating is by direct radiant electric, direct radiant gas or direct warm air use 0.5 in place of 0.2. This is because with these methods of heating less heat is absorbed by the fabric during the relatively short preheat periods and consequently more heating is required to return to acceptable conditions.)

Use Factor = 1 when the accommodation is used — with or without heating.

(In both calculations, where the occupation is, for example, fortnightly, take half of the appropriate factor.)

EXAMPLE OF HEATING AND USE FACTOR CALCULATION FOR A HALL

	Morning	*Afternoon*	*Evening*	*Heating Factor*	*Use Factor*
Sunday	X		X	1.2	2
Monday				nil	nil
Tuesday		X	O	1.0	2
Wednesday			X	1.0	1
Thursday	X	O	O	1.0	3
Friday	X	X	X	1.4	3
Saturday				nil	nil
		Heating Factor		5.6	
		Use Factor			11

TARGET MAXIMUM ANNUAL CONSUMPTION OF ENERGY FOR MAIN HEATING

The following example makes use of information derived from calculations such as the above and also uses approximate volumes. This example assumes that all buildings are heated by the same system. If there are separate heating systems where consumption can be measured and related to each, then a separate calculation should be done for the accommodation relating to each separate system.

CHURCH WITH TWO HALLS ALL HEATED BY THE SAME SYSTEM

	Volume m^3	Heating Factor	Weekly Heated Volume m^3
Church	3,800	1.0	3,800
Hall 'A'	1,200	5.6	6,720
Hall 'B'	600	4.2	2,520
Total Weekly Heated Volume (WHV) =			13,040

The *Weekly Heated Volume* (WHV) m^3 is then inserted in the appropriate formula as follows. (For checking old records – One Therm = 29.3kWh.)

(NOTE: 'kWh of gas' cannot be compared with 'kWh of electricity' because virtually all of the electricity used becomes useful heat without any significant loss, whereas there is a loss to atmosphere in all flued gas burning appliances. In the figures below it will be found that the difference is generally greater than theoretical full load efficiency figures would suggest. This is primarily because there are increased losses in gas fired equipment under part load conditions.)

CENTRAL HEATING SYSTEMS

Oil Fired Boiler   WHV $\times$ 0.8 + 1100   = Target maximum annual consumption in litres of oil.

Gas Fired Boiler $\quad$ WHV $\times$ 8.8 + 11700 = Target maximum
(Natural Gas) $\qquad\qquad\qquad\qquad\qquad$ annual consumption in
$\qquad\qquad\qquad\qquad\qquad\qquad\qquad\qquad$ kWh of gas.

Condensing Boiler WHV $\times$ 8.1 + 10800 = Target maximum
(Natural Gas) $\qquad\qquad\qquad\qquad\qquad$ annual consumption in
$\qquad\qquad\qquad\qquad\qquad\qquad\qquad\qquad$ kWh of gas.

Electric Boiler $\quad$ WHV $\times$ 6.7 + 9000 $\;$ = Target maximum
$\qquad\qquad\qquad\qquad\qquad\qquad\qquad$ annual consumption in
$\qquad\qquad\qquad\qquad\qquad\qquad\qquad\qquad$ kWh of electricity.

DIRECT ELECTRIC HEATING

Convectors $\qquad$ WHV $\times$ 5.3 $\qquad\qquad$ = Target maximum
$\qquad\qquad\qquad\qquad\qquad\qquad\qquad$ annual consumption in
$\qquad\qquad\qquad\qquad\qquad\qquad\qquad\qquad$ kWh of electricity.

Pew Heating $\qquad$ WHV $\times$ 4.6 $\qquad\qquad$ = Target maximum
(plus supplementary $\qquad\qquad\qquad\qquad\qquad$ annual consumption in
convectors) $\qquad\qquad\qquad\qquad\qquad\qquad\qquad$ kWh of electricity.

Radiant $\qquad\qquad$ WHV $\times$ 3.5 $\qquad\qquad$ = Target maximum
$\qquad\qquad\qquad\qquad\qquad\qquad\qquad$ annual consumption in
$\qquad\qquad\qquad\qquad\qquad\qquad\qquad\qquad$ kWh of electricity.

DIRECT GAS HEATING (Natural Gas)

Convectors and $\quad$ WHV $\times$ 8.2 $\qquad\qquad$ = Target maximum
Indirect Warm $\qquad\qquad\qquad\qquad\qquad\qquad$ annual consumption in
Air $\qquad\qquad\qquad\qquad\qquad\qquad\qquad\qquad$ kWh of gas.

Direct Warm Air $\;$ WHV $\times$ 7.6 $\qquad\qquad$ = Target maximum
$\qquad\qquad\qquad\qquad\qquad\qquad\qquad$ annual consumption in
$\qquad\qquad\qquad\qquad\qquad\qquad\qquad\qquad$ kWh of gas.

Radiant Tubes $\quad$ WHV $\times$ 6.5 $\qquad\qquad$ = Target maximum
$\qquad\qquad\qquad\qquad\qquad\qquad\qquad$ annual consumption in
$\qquad\qquad\qquad\qquad\qquad\qquad\qquad\qquad$ kWh of gas.

LPG is delivered in litres if being put in a tank, or in kilograms if in bottles. A litre of LPG is approximately equal to 7 kWh of natural gas. A kilogram is approximately equal to 14 kWh of natural gas. (When comparing costs with oil it is useful to remember that a litre of gas oil or kerosene contains about 10.5 kWh, *ie* about 50% more energy than a litre of LPG.)

TARGET MAXIMUM ANNUAL CONSUMPTION OF ELECTRICITY FOR PURPOSES OTHER THAN MAIN HEATING
(*ie* lighting, cooking, water heating, portable heaters)

The following example is based on the USE FACTOR as calculated above.

Example: Church with two halls all on a common meter for general purpose electricity.

	Area (square meters)		Use Factor		Weekly Used Area
Church	550	×	1	=	550
Hall A	320	×	11	=	3,520
Hall B	170	×	5	=	850
	Total Weekly Used Area			=	4,920

The *Weekly Used Area* × 2.5 = Target maximum consumption of electricity for purposes other than main heating.

In the example above 4,920 × 2.5 = 12,300 kWh.

This consumption will certainly be exceeded in historic buildings where lights are on for prolonged periods for the benefit of visitors. Floodlighting and extensive security lighting has not been allowed for in these calculations.

MONITORING

Having established target figures by the above method, or at the very least having obtained accurate figures for the previous year to give a base line, it is then necessary to keep track of what is happening.

Experience has shown that most people who try to do this get bogged down in so many figures that they lose their meaning. There is a strong temptation to record weekly figures and almost inevitably all that happens is that the consumption for each week is extracted. This can be interesting but it is suggested that it is much more likely to be meaningful, and the task more likely to be maintained, if readings are taken monthly and given due consideration relative to targets.

To make this easier the following table provides an approximate means of splitting up your first annual figure to show about how much of it should be allocated to each month. This will give some indication, without waiting for a whole year, as to whether readings being taken are tending to be higher or lower than target. Inaccuracies will be reduced if you work accumulatively from the start of the year, or say the beginning of September, rather than comparing on a month by month basis. The figures in the tables exclude July and August where consumption is usually small enough to be absorbed into the June and September figures without significant error. They are based on an average Scottish situation.

When readings are taken in the second and subsequent years you will have your own record of monthly figures which should be used as the basis for allocating the target. It is probable that you will have two different percentage allocations for heating and General purpose electricity.

While the value of monthly readings has been emphasized because they give a better feel for what is happening, and avoid the likelihood of despair because of a missed reading, it is recognized that there will be variations in the number of Sundays in a month which will obviously cause differences. This is why the cumulative figure is the most useful.

Figures taken from electricity and gas company accounts are very limited in value. At best, there are probably no more than two readings from each meter per year and at worst not even one. You should always make a point of checking estimates and sending in corrections if the difference is significant.

Month	%	Cumulative %
January	15	15
February	14	29
March	13	42
April	10	52
May	7	59
June	4	63
September	4	67
October	7	74
November	12	86
December	14	100

or

Month	%	Cumulative %
September	4	4
October	7	11
November	12	23
December	14	37
January	15	52
February	14	66
March	13	79
April	10	89
May	7	96
June	4	100

CASE NOTES

In one of the few modern and highly insulated church complexes surveyed, it was found that they were using twice as much gas and six times as much electricity as the above calculation would have given as targets. Investigation revealed design and installation errors in the complex heating control system. Once the faults had been corrected the figures came well inside the targets.

A congregation had a very enthusiastic member who read every meter at least once a week and often daily. They were swamped with information. Unfortunately they had no basis of comparison and though they knew all about what they were using they did not realize that this was about twice as much as was necessary. Once a target was calculated and the problem identified a few simple modifications saved thousands of pounds.

(13)
LIGHTING 1:
THE HISTORY AND THE PRESENT

Since the introduction of the coiled coil tungsten filament lamp in the early 1930s, lighting in churches has changed very little. Church lighting cannot be a simple function of lumens per sq metre or lux on a reading plane. Church lighting has to be sympathetic with the church liturgy and harmonize with the hymns and the singing and the music. Lighting must enhance the architecture of the church and indeed be part of the architecture itself. Up to the early 1930s it was the oil lamp and the gas mantle, but when these were replaced with the tungsten filament lamp this has been the predominant light source to achieve these objectives.

Lighting design and an understanding of the science of lighting in the 1930s was contained in a booklet published by ELMA (Electrical Lamp Manufacturers Association) but over the years, as the knowledge of lighting progressed into a science, Codes of Practice were produced until by the 1960s legal recognition was being given to new standards of light levels for commercial buildings and factories. Light levels in churches were being provided in these Codes of Practice at 60 lux to 100 lux, but the source of light was still the tungsten filament lamp and the price to achieve the higher levels was a proliferation of these lamps in gracious chandeliers or in specular or mirror type reflector fittings, and this introduced a new dimension into consideration for church lighting, *ie* maintenance and lamp replacement.

Lumen — a unit of quantity of light or luminous flux emitted from a light source per second

Lux — luminous flux or lumens per square metre

1 — lumen/ft^2 = 10.76 lux

1 — lux = .093 lumens per foot^2

By the 1970s and 1980s a new generation of churchgoer was registering an awareness in regard to church lighting. Members educated in the 1950s and 1960s in levels of light at 150 lux and thence 300 lux or more in offices or colleges, with a new profession of lighting engineers providing designed lighting with a restricted glare index, and with a provision of designed comfort lighting environment, this new generation began to be aware of the inadequacy of the 30 or 40 lux in the local church.

Parallel with this came the heart cry of the volunteer brigade perilously poised on ladders and chasing the never-ending trail of tungsten filament lamp replacement and demanding something different.

Moving into the 1980s there became a general awareness of the combined problems of inadequate light levels, and difficulties of maintenance, leading to the situation as applies at the present day.

THE PRESENT

The majority of parish churches still have lighting installations based on lighting technology available from the past and utilizing light sources derived from the 1930s. The older members of congregations, while perhaps still having a sentimental attachment to the gracious chandelier, no longer are prepared to accept the challenges of access to inaccessible light fittings, and the younger sections of congregations are becoming aware that the standards which were acceptable 30 years ago are no longer acceptable today. Congregations are also becoming increasingly aware of the advances in lighting technology and are searching for alternatives. As a result of research in development over the past 10 to 15 years, new light sources are available which can help Fabric Conveners to replace the outdated present day lighting installations with a higher level in functional light levels and at the same time maintain the necessary sympathy with the church service and be compatible with the architecture of the church.

ALTERNATIVES AVAILABLE

Tungsten filament lamps

In an energy conscious world of the lumen per watt efficiency of fluorescent, compact fluorescent tubes, and discharge lamps, the tungsten filament lamp with a lumen efficiency at 13 lumens per watt is slowly being consigned to archaeology. A lamp life at 1000 hours, compared compared to 6000 hours for fluorescent and compact fluorescent tubes, and 12,000 hours for discharge lamps, is accelerating the process. The present day recommended lighting levels in the order of 100–150 lux for churches are almost impossible to achieve using these lamps unless by multi-light chandeliers with 150 watt lamps or by very high wattage lamps, which, with their associated glare and heat loss, are rapidly going out of use for general lighting.

Tungsten halogen lamps

The tungsten halogen lamp employs a conventional tungsten filament with the envelope containing small amounts of halogen, which, combined with the tungsten evaporated from the filament, produce a lumen output more than twice the tungsten filament lamp output at 25–30 lumens per watt. At 240 volts this type of lamp has particular applications for small floodlights and it has been used for lighting of church interiors, particularly when lighting from the side of the church. However, the quality of light produced is cold and, unless shielded and louvred, can cause a degree of discomfort to the congregation from associated glare. Lamp life very rarely exceeds 1500 hours.

The most recent development in tungsten halogen is the 12 volt dichroic reflector type lamps, where the lamp itself is a small 50mm diameter reflector. The reflector lamps, with fixed beam spreads varying from 12° to 36°, provide at 50 watt the equivalent to a 120 watt 240 volt PAR 38 reflector type tungsten lamp. The main application, however, is for local display or spotlights located adjacent to lecterns, or to highlight memorials or statues or to emphasize arches, ceiling or special features.

Fluorescent tubes

Everyone will be familiar with the fluorescent tube in commercial buildings: 38mm tubes with luminous efficiency at 70–80 lumens per watt, 26mm tubes with luminous efficiency of 80–90 lumens per watt and the new generation of fluorescent control circuits coming forward which converts the mains supply to high frequency, producing even greater efficiencies, all in comparison to the 12–13 lumens per watt from tungsten filament lamps. Add to this a minimum lamp life at 6000 hours (and more than this if switching is not too frequent) the fluorescent lamp would appear to be the answer to lighting problems if all that is to be achieved is a functional level of light. Fluorescent lamps provide a cold ambience which is out of keeping with a warmth which one would expect in a church service. 1500mm, 1800mm and 2400mm tubes with acrylic clip-on diffusers in the full glare of a congregation, present an unwieldy appearance which, it is suggested, is not really in keeping with church architecture.

Fluorescent tubes can, however, provide a pleasing effect if built into the architecture of the building to the point that tubes themselves are hidden to reflect light either from the ceiling or from the side wall and they can be used in this context if the opportunity presents itself, *ie* providing upward light from cross beams within the church or from coves or cornices at high level.

Clearly fluorescent lighting will have a place in perimeter passages or in church halls, although if the church halls are used for sports purposes, the fittings should be provided with polycarbonate fixed diffusers or wire guards.

Flourescent compact tubes

In the last ten years there have been considerable advances in the manufacture of compact fluorescent lamps with inbuilt electronic control gear to replace the tungsten filament lamps.

The compact fluorescent tubes listed below are all appropriate to church use as direct replacement of tungsten filament lamps, ES or BC

Manufacturer	Wattage	Equivalent Tungsten Wattage	Lumen Output	Diameter mm	Length mm
Osram, Sylvania					
Deluxe EL	7	40	370	58	145
(BC or ES)	11	60	550	58	145
	15	75	830	58	175
	20	100	1100	58	207
	23	2–60	1330	58	207
				Circle	
Osram Circolux EL	18	75	920	165	100
	24	100	1330	165	100
	32	150	1850	216	100
Sylvania –	15	75	830	58	142
Triple Turn Lamp	20	100	1100	58	162
	23	2–60	1330	58	162
Osram, Sylvania					
Compacta	18	75	830	73	171
(BC or ES)	25	100	1100	73	181
Philips	9	40	450	74	151
SL	13	60	650	74	161
BC or ES	18	75	900	74	171
	25	100	1200	74	181
Philips	7	40	400	46	161
PLC-E	11	60	600	46	161
(BC or ES)	15	75	900	46	195
	20	100	1200	46	210
Thorn	16	75	925	140 × 140 square	
2D	28	150	1850	Ht with ballast 90mm	
	38	200	2600	205 × 205 square	

Lamp life 8000–10,000 hours.

lampholders. Current advancement in 1993 will lead to even further reduction in dimensions. In some cases two colours are available, warm white and white. Warm white is the nearest colour to tungsten filament lamps and is the colour for use in churches.

The above lists Osram, Philips, Thorn and Sylvania as suppliers in the United Kingdom, but another supplier who can supply similar lamps is GE Lighting.

Manufacturers can change over the years and there will be frequent additions to the list under the impetus of competition, but the above can be taken as a basis from which replacement selections for compact fluorescent tubes can be made.

There is another range of 15–25 watt fluorescent tubes with separate control gear. These cannot be used as direct replacement for tungsten filament lamps and are mainly used for installation in light fittings such as the shallow depth fittings suitable for church undergalleries.

Mercury blended tungsten ballast

The wattage range of this lamp is at 100, 160, 250 and 500, but the main application for this type of lamp with a tungsten ballast is that it is interchangeable with an existing tungsten filament lamp with BC holder. The output of the 160 watt at 3000 lumens compares to 2000 lumens for the 150 watt tungsten filament lamp. The colour of this lamp brings it into the range of the cold fluorescent lamp which is not very acceptable for church lighting. The lamp life at 6000 hours means a church life at almost 30 years and it is a simple method of upgrading church lighting, particularly if located behind a white opalescent enclosure. The size of this lamp at 177mm × 77mm diameter may preclude accommodation in all existing fittings.

Metal halide lamps

Metal halide lamps range from 50, 70, 100, 150, 175, 400 watts, with two ranges of colour, white and warm white. It is essential that the latter range, *ie* warm white, be adopted for churches. The principal advantage of this lamp is that the lumen output is almost five times the lumen output for the equivalent tungsten filament lamp, *ie* 150 watt metal halide is 11500, 150 watt tungsten 2000 lumens. With the recommended standard of lighting within churches having increased since the 1930s almost five times, this does mean that the standard of lighting in existing churches can be achieved by a simple replacement of the light source using the existing spacing of the light fittings.

Lamp life is 10 to 12 times the life of a tungsten filament lamp at 10,000–12,000 hours. This cannot be guaranteed and is dependent on the frequency of switching, but for church use where switching may be only four or five times in a week, this figure does infer that effectively there should be no lamp replacement in the church over a considerable number of years.

The lamps are single ended, which would be applicable to pendant light fittings, and also double ended which is applicable to floodlights with specular or mirror-type reflectors and for uplighters where this lamp perhaps comes into its own in that the high lumen output can be reflected off a cream coloured ceiling. This has a particular attraction for churches with plaster ceilings where the entire ceiling area becomes an effective luminaire.

A warning in regard to these lamps is that while the colour rendering is satisfactory, there is a degree of colour instability and within the same batch of lamps there can be varying degrees, albeit slight, in the colour temperature.

These lamps do require control ballasts and capacitors. These are contained in control boxes measuring 290mm × 80mm × 60mm high, weighing 3kg, and space must be found for this equipment. Lamp igniters to strike the initial arc should be contained in the light fitting.

High pressure sodium

This lamp, available in 70, 100, 150, 250, 400, 600 watts, has a colour, particularly with the high pressure sodium deluxe lamp above 100 watt (HP SON DL), which is a warmer colour than the average tungsten filament lamp. The general effect within the church is to produce a warm pink ambience to a church interior and acuity. In particular, reading black on white, as with bibles or hymn books, is enhanced.

Technical details for lamp life and lumen output are similar to metal halide lamps.

Comparison Table – Metal Halide and High Pressure Sodium

The comparison table is provided below to show the light output in lumens of HP SON or halide lamps, with the lumen output for equivalent wattage tungsten filament lamps.

	HP SON or Halide Lumen Output	Equivalent Wattage Tungsten Filament Lumen Output
70–75 watt	5300	890
100 watt	8800	1260
150 watt	11,000	2000

CONSERVATION

The significant factor in all the lamp sources provided above is the tremendous improvement in the light output and lumens per watt from the discharge fluorescent or the HP SON and metal halide lamps compared to the equivalent wattage of tungsten filament lamps.

In commercial offices, schools, supermarkets, factories and all buildings in continuous hourly use requiring continuous lighting, advantage is taken to utilize this increase in lumens per watt efficiency to provide lighting to reach the stipulated standard now recognized in the Code of the Chartered Institution of Building Services, mentioned in the following chapter, but also to reduce the heat kilowatt load in buildings. It is the build-up of heating in buildings which provides one of the principal difficulties in achieving environmental building control resulting in the necessity to have compensating cooling or air conditioning.

Achieving the present-day standards of lighting level with the improved lamp efficiency means a reduction in wattage for the higher standard of lighting level and therefore means an effective saving in consumption which is paid for on a watt-hour basis. In commercial buildings and throughout the country the simple tungsten filament lamp has largely disappeared and has been replaced with discharge lamps. Savings are shown in consumer accounts which in turn are reflected back to reduce power station demand, and reduced power station demand means a reduction in prime fuel consumption, *ie* conservation.

With an average use of a church at two to four hours per week (or in a year of 52 weeks, 104–208 hours) replacing a tungsten filament lamp at 70p to £1.00 with a compact fluorescent lamp at £15 to £20 is difficult to justify to a treasurer. The reduction in consumption charges is not impressive enough to offset the higher capital outlay unless over a considerable number of years. The main incentive is to have lamps with increased lumen output and effectively no replacement. The bonus follows with less consumption in electricity. However, progressively the compact fluorescent lamps will reduce in cost and the unit charges for electricity will increase in cost. For churches, therefore, conservation will assume an increased significance over future years.

Church halls and ancillary areas on the other hand provide a better case for reducing electricity costs and most churches are already familiar with fluorescent tubes with their greater light output for these areas where the requirement of achieving a sympathy with church architecture does not exercise a control in the selection of light source.

There is justification for employing the more efficient discharge lamps with increased lumen output and effective elimination of frequent lamp replacement, but discerning church management should seek to replace tungsten filament lamps (if necessary as a gradual process) over the years to achieve the additional bonus of reduction in consumption of electricity, which in turn means reduced power station fuel consumption and progressively the church will be making its contribution to the reduction in national fuel consumption.

14

LIGHTING 2: THE FUTURE

With these new light sources available the question is how do we address ourselves to improving the standards which exist today?

There are basic recommended levels of lighting given in the Code provided by the Chartered Institution of Building Services Engineers, which now incorporates the Illuminating Engineering Society. The Code is obtainable from the Chartered Institution of Building Services Engineers, Delta House, 222 Balham High Road, London, SW12 9BS. There is also an excellent booklet provided by the Church House Publishing, Great Smith Street, London, SW1P 3BN.

The levels for illumination given in this latter booklet seem more realistic than the higher levels given in the CIBSE Code, when consideration is given to the solemnity of church liturgy requiring a suitable respectful lighting. Recommended levels are given as:

Body of Church, Nave and Transepts – 100–200 lux
Pulpit, Lecturn, Choir and Chancel – 150–300 lux

The imperial measurement is in foot candles per sq ft or lumens per sq ft. The metric measurement is in lux and 1 lumen per sq ft approximately equals 11 lux: *ie* divide the above figures by 11 to achieve a near enough value in foot candles or lumens per sq ft.

A simple basic formula can be used by Fabric Conveners as a guide to assessing what their existing lighting levels are and what they will need to achieve the above levels. This formula is as follows:

Lumens/sq metre, *ie* lux,

$$= \frac{\text{No of lamps} \times \text{lumens/lamp} \times \text{utilisation factor}}{\text{Area in sq metres}}$$

The lumens per lamp is easily obtainable from manufacturers' catalogues and a typical list is provided on page 113 for compact fluorescent lamps and on page 116 for HP SON and metal halide lamps.

The utilisation factor depends on many variables; *ie* light output of fittings (upward and downward), reflection values of ceilings, walls and floor, ratio of length, width and height of room, distribution and height of fittings above the reading plane. All these variables are provided in lighting design manuals, but on the basis that all that is wanted by a fabric convener is a rough guide to allow him to assess fittings and lamps required to achieve 100–150 lux, the following factors will provide a basis:

Where the height of the fitting above the reading plane is 2–4 metres, as in church undergalleries with a bright reflecting ceiling, cream or white, a suitable factor would be .45; and for a dull reflecting ceiling, blue or brown .3 −.35.

Where the height of the fitting above the reading plan is 6–10 metres, as in the open area, chancel, well areas, or above galleries, again with a bright reflecting ceiling, a factor of .35 could apply; and for a dull reflecting ceiling or brown wood ceilings, which occur in many churches, a utilisation factor of .3 would be appropriate.

It must be made clear that this is not a recipe for an accurate design and is only intended as a guide. In a church, the areas would be separated out as nave, transepts, under gallery, over gallery, chancel or communion table area and foyer or reception hall.

Nowadays, there are computer programmes which take into account all the variables involved in arriving at the utilization factor and lighting fitting suppliers will usually provide a free service giving light levels, provided they are given individual church areas, heights and locations of fittings, and if possible plan and elevation drawings.

EXPERT ADVICE

It is repeated that the above formula is only a guide to functional light levels and the ideal is to have advice based on a knowledge of the more detailed assessment of the utilisation factor, a sensitive appreciation as to the balance which church lighting should achieve in relation to the liturgy of service and the architecture of the church itself. A practical experience is also necessary as to the requirements for maintaining the installation when completed, *ie* the difficulty of access to fittings over pews. A financial awareness is also essential having regard to the church treasurer's outlook in regard to a realistic appreciation of money available and costing for the lighting installation.

The average parish church will have to be realistic and appreciate that, in present day terms, supplying and installing 20–30 light fittings does not constitute a large financial contract, especially if achieved through competition. Fitting suppliers or contractors will not have enough profit margin to provide the most expert of advice and the cost of surveys, so, whether it be expert architect, expert lighting engineer, expert local electrician, and particularly the inevitable expert on the church committee, the rule has to be 'beware of experts'. Ask to see a system of lighting previously designed by the expert.

Lighting is not simply lumens per sq metre or lux. It is an art, it is subjective, there are many opinions and it does pay to be questioning in the acceptance of advice. If possible try and seek out two or three alternatives from different lighting fitting suppliers or from architects or lighting engineers.

If the schemes answer the following criteria there is hope that there will be the basis for an acceptable lighting proposal.

(1) Will the lumen level be equally distributed over the individual church areas and be adequate, *ie* near to 100 lux at reading level?

(2) Will the result be sympathetic to the liturgy of the church service (*ie* no harsh lighting)? Are fluorescent lights kept to upward lighting or cove lighting?

(3) Will the church architecture be shown off to advantage, *ie* in a high church is there upward light? Will the lighting, when completed, effectively model the church architecture to give a designed appearance?

(4) Is the cost of the scheme compatible with the available church finances or can an adequate result be achieved at less cost?

(5) Can the lighting scheme conform to the existing wiring of the

church or does a new scheme require considerable additional expensive wiring?

(6) Will the new scheme be energy conscious using compact fluorescent or discharge lamps?

(7) Will the new scheme recognize ease of access for maintenance from volunteer church members?

HOW TO IMPROVE ON LIGHT LEVELS USING EXISTING INSTALLATIONS

Even from 30 to 50 years ago there was an awareness of correct spacing of light fittings to provide uniform light distribution, however low, with the use of tungsten filament lamps. In most parish churches therefore there is an existing framework to build upon by using the new high output high pressure discharge lamps to improve the lighting.

It will be apparent from the Comparison Table on page 116 above that there are now two light sources which, using the existing framework of lighting points, can increase the light levels by 5 or 6 times without an increase in the wattage, or alternatively a single 150 watt high pressure discharge lamp can replace a 5-light 150 watt chandelier.

As indicated on pages 115 and 116 above, the lamp life of these lamps is very important at 11,000 hours, which, in terms of average church use, means theoretically 20 to 30 years without replacement. A suitable fitting to accommodate these discharge lamps is the timeless glass sphere with 70 watt high pressure lamps contained within 250mm spheres, 100 watt in 300–400mm spheres and 150 watt in 400 or 450 mm spheres. Alternatively a simple replacement can be achieved if the existing fittings are large enough to accept discharge lamps.

These lamps require control gear and in churches with attic roofs or roof voids the control gear can be concealed in the roof space if kept clear from the woodwork by cable tray to avoid the risk of fire and provided that proper access and walkways are installed.

In churches with roof beams the control gear can usually rest on the tie or collar beam, but on flat roofs there is no alternative other than to have a control gear box secured to the roof with a $\frac{1}{2}''$ space for ventilation and painted out in the same colour as the roof.

With the high lumen output from the discharge lamps there can be a consequent glare unless properly enclosed and to limit this glare it is a recommendation that the lamp wattage within the church should be limited to 150 watt. Above this wattage, even in a 450mm sphere, there is a high degree of glare to the point of discomfort.

A point of warning must be given in regard to the high pressure SON lamp in that this lamp does take time to mature from an orange colour to the normal warm pink output, and with the use of this lamp at perhaps only one or two hours per week, it can be a year before this warm pink ambience develops and thereafter progressively the output becomes almost white tungsten in colour. A cautionary word must also be given in regard to the colour rendering for the high pressure sodium lamp in that with a church decor in orange or red, HP SON or HP SON deluxe should not be used.

The metal halide lamp, which can have a place in churches where the woodwork is predominantly dark, is available in colours of white and warm white. Of these two alternatives only the latter should be used and this is still equivalent to the colour of fluorescent warm white lamps.

Both the metal halide and the HP SON lamps are discharge lamps and as such have a reactive or inductive current which requires that any existing old-fashioned switches should be checked and replaced by 15–20 amp switches or circuit breakers.

For the church treasurer, a guide to the cost of a glass sphere, 150 watt lamp and associated control gear, would be approximately £280–300 (excluding VAT) at 1993 prices. Polycarbonate spheres can be used instead of glass, with a reduction in cost.

Undergalleries

In existing churches with undergalleries there is very rarely a correct distribution of light fittings. An absolute necessity is that the distance between the point source fittings should not exceed 1.5 times the distance between ceiling and the reading plane. If the distance between the undergallery ceiling and the hymn books when the congregation is standing up is at 2.5m, then the distance between fittings should not exceed 3.5–4.0m. This is essential to avoid a differential in light level between fittings and will apply over the whole area beneath the gallery.

Before installing new fittings these distances must be checked out, but usually additional lighting points can be installed by lifting floor boards from above and wiring in PVC twin and earth cable at 1.5mm². Point source fittings, *ie* sphere type ceiling or short pendant with 70 watt HP SON lamps (output 5000 lumens) as distinct from fluorescent fittings are suitable at heights above three metres from the floor. For heights below three metres there are close ceiling fittings projecting no more than 110mm having two compact fluorescent tubes at 18 watt or 24 watt (2600 lumens or 3380 lumens). There are also similar fittings housing the Thorn Compact 2D lamp 28 watt or 38 watt (1800 lumens and 2650 lumens). The nearest equivalent tungsten filament lamps for these fittings is:

	Compact Fluorescent		Tungsten Filament	
	Lumen Output		Lumen Output	
2–18 watt		2600 lumens	200 watt	2730 lumens
2–24 watt		3380 lumens	200 watt	2730 lumens
2D lamp −28 watt		1850 lumens	150 watt	2030 lumens
2D lamp −38 watt		2600 lumens	200 watt	2730 lumens

It is essential for colour rendering that these compact lamps should all be warm white, this being the nearest colour to tungsten filament lamps.

It has to be acknowledged that the problem of undergallery lighting can be most easily solved by the use of 1800mm or 2400mm fluorescent tubes with a lumen output in the order of 6000 lumens and 9000 lumens respectively. The length of fluorescent tube at 2400mm (8ft) also can overcome the

$$\text{ratio} \quad \frac{\text{distance between fittings}}{\text{distance ceiling to reading plane}} \quad \text{problem}$$

without additional lighting points and this is a simple cheap and functional way to increase the lumen level of light beneath galleries at a cost similar to the compact fluorescent fittings referred to above. Such a cost would appeal to a church treasurer, but in terms of compatibility with the architecture of a church and the colour ambience, the fluorescent tube would not be advocated as the correct answer for undergallery lighting.

Churches with white or cream plaster ceilings

A number of churches have plaster ceilings and this does present an opportunity to the lighting designer to use the white reflective surface from the ceiling as a luminaire to provide a diffused light throughout the whole church and still use the existing lighting points. If the ceiling is of the barrel vaulted or fan vaulted plaster type, this provides an additional incentive not only to use the ceiling as a lighting luminaire for the whole church, but to highlight the fan ceiling with uplighters and to effectively integrate lighting with the architecture of the church and thereby present a unified designed architectural lighting appearance throughout the whole church and in sympathy with the liturgy of the church service.

If the plasterwork is decorative, as in the church of St Martin in the Fields, London, or has white plaster between the ribs in the fan vaulting, as at Haddington Parish Church, then it is imperative that these featues be exploited with upward illumination, and the HP SON lamp and the metal halide lamp with their high lumen output are a perfect source to provide directed light on to the plaster ceilings to give a reflected light at reading level in the order of 120–200 lux.

Bowl type opalescent fittings with the glass 'flashed' with a circular fluorescent tube, but with a 150 watt metal halide lamp directed upwards with the distance between fittings being equal to 1.5–2.0 times the suspension height, and a white or cream ceiling, the lumen output which can be expected in a church 7–8m high from floor to ceiling can be at 120–200 lux.

The same effect can be achieved with the simple opalescent sphere which has an upward light at 30% and downward light at 70% in utilizing the roof plasterwork as an architectural luminaire.

LIGHTING FOR CHURCHES TO BE REWIRED

Testing of wiring

Church wiring should be checked by an approved contractor, *ie* approved by the National Inspection Council or the Electrical Contractors Association, to ensure compliance with the IEE Regulations and to ensure continuous safety is preserved. A check must be made once every year.

If a church is to be re-wired on grounds of age and deterioration of wiring or non-compliance with the IEE Regulations, and there is no requirement to re-use the existing conduit system, then a church has complete freedom of action in the design of an alternative system of lighting. The systems will probably vary according to the architecture of the buildings, and only the basic principles can be given to help a church in its consideration of lighting schemes. These criteria are listed on page 120, with the additional guide for new installations, that if the old system of lighting points has been satisfactory in the past then do not change just for the sake of change. Consider first selecting alternative light sources which can be applied to the old distribution points.

If the church is to be re-wired with a repeat or a near repeat of the existing lighting point distribution the advice pertaining to light sources available and given above relating to replacement light sources for existing installations will still apply.

Lighting from the side of the church

The lighting of churches with high roofs, pitched or flat, with a definition of high as being selected arbitrarily at 30–50ft (10–15m) or more, always presents a difficulty of access to suspended fittings, particularly if there is no roof void from which chain suspended fittings can be lowered. The hazards in obtaining frequent access to pendant fittings (particularly with tungsten filament lamps) located over pews, has led to many churches when contemplating replacement wiring schemes to seek what is a current fashionable answer, *ie* to provide lighting from both sides of the nave area where the fittings can be made accessible by a ladder placed against the wall.

The introduction of the discharge lamp with small point source or linear source of light which can be controlled by specular or mirror-type reflectors has tended to encourage this method of approach, but there are cautionary guidelines to be given when contemplating this type of lighting:

(1) Discharge lamps, or tungsten halogen lamps in a floodlight with a specular mirror reflector, have a concentrated output confined to well-controlled beam angles and direct lighting downwards from either side of the congregation area only ceates discomfort glare unless shielded by louvres opening flaps or 'barn' doors. Pointing the fittings towards the communion table avoids discomfort to the congregation but blinds the minister and effectively flattens the whole area of worship under a concentrated blast of light.

(2) Unless the roof space above the fittings is also provided with an upward light the congregation will experience a claustrophobic or tunnel effect, and the rule must be that for every specular reflector fitting pointing downwards there should be a similar, though perhaps lower wattage light source pointing up. Clearly this requirement has a considerable impact on cost of the new installation.

(3) Again, with the tight and accurate beam angle at 12° or 30°, as applies in quite a number of fittings, unless these fittings are located at a height 1.5 times the width of the nave or central area, there cannot be an even distribution of light. Walking around a church provided with this type of lighting with a light meter, the light readings can fluctuate within a few feet and the congregation in such a church can be observed drifting gently into areas where the light is strongest.

(4) Floodlights, even of the compact size, are difficult to integrate with the architectural line of a church, particularly if surface mounted, unless partially obscured at the top of columns or hidden in coves.

Parish churches which follow a simple gothic principle, with the nave area as a main vault supported on columns with capitals and flanked by vaulted aisles, provide opportunity for side lighting to 'shape' the architecture by designed lighting from the sides.

Uplighters located at triforium or clerestory level or at capital level, or in rib or fan vaulted ceilings at corbel level, help to emphasize the architecture of the church, and the same principle can apply in smaller churches where the 75 watt tungsten halogen dichroic lamp has applications for architectural enhancement. This type of designed appearance lighting does require advice from recognized and accepted experts.

In the context of church lighting, specular reflector fittings floodlights, particularly with discharge lamps or reflector lamps, should only be considered if they can be guaranteed to provide:

(1) Upward light.
(2) Uniform distribution at reading level.
(3) Without glare either to minister or congregation.
(4) Floodlights which integrate with the church architecture and are not obtrustive on the side walls.

However, lighting from the side need not necessarily be carried out using specular reflectors. Where height precludes long suspensions over the central or nave area, there have been successful installations where the light fittings have been suspended from wrought iron wall brackets projecting approximately 1m, and provided that the height of the bracket is at least 1.5 times the width of the nave, wall bracket suspensions from both sides of the nave can provide uniform distribution.

If the church to be re-wired has a white or cream plaster roof then the advantage of rewiring can be taken to create new lighting points on the side walls to accept uplighters employing 150 watt metal halide or 150 watt HP SON linear discharge lamps. The fittings have asymmetrical specular mirror reflectors which throw the light outwards on to the white ceiling which diffuses the lighting and provides a mellow white or pink ambience throughout the church. An example of this is at Busby West Church, south of Glasgow. This church, measuring 15m long × 11m wide and 9m high, and with a U-shaped gallery, has 4–150 watt metal halide lamps in wall uplighters located at new lighting points on either side of the church, installed under the new rewiring scheme. The distance between fittings is 3.5 metres and the distance from the ceiling 1.5–2.0 metres.

Lighting level in the communion table area was at 180 lux. Similar uplighters with 70 watt metal halide lamps were located below the

U-shaped gallery, again 3.5m apart and 1.2–1.5m below the gallery ceiling and provided similar levels. The complete effect throughout the church demonstrates an unobtrusive lighting, integrated with the architecture, to provide an inviting glare free ambience.

DIMMING

Some churches consider that dimming of the lighting can provide an atmosphere conducive to worship. The only lamp sources which can contribute to achieving this with a degree of technical simplicity is the tungsten filament and the tungsten halogen lamp.

The disadvantages of these lamps are outlined above on page 111 and the arguments to support the dimming do have to be powerful to influence departing from the discharge lamp lighting solution. A compromise can be achieved by installing a separate form of tungsten filament or tungsten halogen lighting to achieve a lower level of atmosphere lighting or to employ pressed glass Par 38 lamps or Par 56 lamps, or even stage lighting spotlights, to highlight nativity plays or orchestral concerts with the main lighting switched off.

Voltage control dimming using bulky resistors or auto-transformers has now been replaced with the electronic switch current control system known as triacs. With this system the current to the lighting units is electronically switched to give pulses of current which can be increased or decreased to vary the average current flow and vary the light output.

Simple controls, up to 6 kilowatt, can be accommodated in two small boxes, 250mm square and 75mm in depth, but at 10–20KW and above the electronic switches are at a larger capacity and are called thyristors. These units are used in large scale stage or television studio lighting. At this high kilowatt level of lighting, or for churches or cathedrals where elaborate perfomances are given, it is almost essential that a firm of specialist lighting suppliers for stage and television lighting should be employed where the lighting equipment can be purchased outright or else hired for the special occasion.

Specialist advice should be sought whatever type of dimming is employed. The current pulses provided by the electronic switch, whether triac or thyristor, are effectively crude blocks of current and in a lighting wiring system can give considerable interference on the magnetic coil hearing aids as used by deaf people. The dimming system requires filter circuits on both the supply and output side of the dimming units. Screening of cables and earthing independent from the main supply earth is also necessary. It should be a contract condition that the contractor provides an interference-free system. Similarly the supplier and installer of magnetic deaf-aid loop systems, which are now extensively used in churches, must undertake to ensure that no interference is experienced if a dimmer system is already in place.

The dimming of fluorescent lamps has advanced considerably over the past few years, particularly with the high frequency lamps and ballasts. Fluorescent dimming, even for compact fluorescent tubes, is therefore available if there should be an appropriate application.

Fluorescent dimming cannot be applied to existing fittings without dismantling the existing control gear.

To date dimming of HP SON lamps and metal halide lamps is not commercially available, but research in the future may make this a possibility.

ACCESS TO FITTINGS

Light sources providing light onto a reading plane must of necessity be located to provide light from above. Light fittings located above require access for maintenance. If the church has a roof void or attic, lighting fittings can be suspended on chains, and by the provision of an additional length of chain can be lowered down to floor level and maintained with safety.

If there is no roof void, then raising and lowering equipment is available using automatic release contacts, winches, pulleys and wire, but unless located with care and discretion the equipment and cable can be unsightly – but this apparatus is ideal where there is no alternative method of lowering fittings to ground level.

Again, if there is no roof void, then tower equipment can be used as 4ft × 2ft and 16ft high or alternatively 4ft × 4ft × 22ft high. This will provide access whether the light fittings are suspended or are

installed as side projectors. Tower access is essential in most circumstances, but it must be borne in mind that an incorrectly built or
mounted tower, particularly when working between pews, could lead to
serious accident.

For churches in Scotland the Church of Scotland insurance contains
inherent restrictions by stipulating under the Personal Accident requirements that no-one over the age of 65 shall operate above ground level.
Every church should seek professional help and advice from the insurance
company and check that Personal Accident insurance is available, but
even then the questionnaire covering Personal Accident insurance for
volunteer workers does impose stringent requirements and is only
available to £5000 maximum, which is negligible in the event of severe
disability caused by a fall. The church insurance company should always
be consulted when any type of work is undertaken both in regard to
Personal Accident insurance and insurance company requirements.

A check should also be made with insurers in regard to Public
Liability Requirements.

The Health and Safety at Work Act is now assuming a greater
importance and relevance to churches, and congregations will have to
accept that they are required under the Act to provide safe premises for
congregations and for employees and contractors. With a particular
application for lighting, there is now a statutory duty for the churches
to ensure safety in relation to access ladders and scaffolding whether
internal or external to the church.

The responsibility for implementing the requirements of the Health
and Safety Act has now been transferred to the District Councils where
advice can be obtained as to the safety of building access or access
equipment. For instance, if the church does have a roof void or attic
accessible for wiring or lighting fitting maintenance, it is a statutory
requirement under the Health and Safety at Work Act, enforceable
by law, to have proper walkways constructed so that congregation
members, employees or external contractors can have safety of access and
movement, together with adequate lighting.

EMERGENCY LIGHTING

Under present day legislation there is a requirement for buildings to have standby or emergency lighting, so that if the main supply lighting should fail, either externally or internal to the building, there is adequate lighting to indicate exits and the escape routes to exits.

For church buildings standby lighting will be provided by individual light fittings, each with batteries to operate small fluorescent lamps and to give a level of lighting along escape routes in the region of .2 lux.

There is a BS specification 5266, but this is subject to varying interpretations by Local Authorities, Firemasters, Fire Prevention Officers and insurance companies and advice will require to be obtained from these sources.

For churches the main criteria are as follows:

(1) Is the church going to be used for orchestral concerts, opera or public entertainment?
(2) Is the church to be available to the general public as well as congregational members?

For church rooms or halls a different set of criteria exist as follows:

(1) Are the church rooms to be used during the day and in the evenings?
(2) Are the church halls to be used for sports activities?
(3) Are the church halls to be used for dances and theatre entertainment?
(4) Are individual committee rooms to be used by church organisations or by external organisations during the day or at night?
(5) Are any of the church rooms or halls to be used as dormitories by youth organisations?

Supplementary questions are:

(6) If all the lights are switched off are the exit doors clearly visible?
(7) Are escape routes clearly visible?
(8) Do all escape doors open outwards?
(9) On exiting from rooms or halls do the external exits have battery lighting and are they free of obstruction?

If any of the answers to questions 1 and 2 for churches, and for questions 1 to 5 for church rooms, is 'Yes', then the advice from the Fire Authority must be obtained, and if the Property Convener cannot give a decisive 'Yes' in answer to supplementary questions 6 to 9, Fire Authority advice is essential.

CONCLUSION

It is hoped that the above, particularly the references to the latest types of lighting sources which are currently available, will define a new set of principles to be followed in church lighting. There can be no authoritative assertions which can be given for the many varied architectural designs for churches and, however careful the deliberations in arriving at solutions, the answer will always be subjective.

In the words of a famous professor of Electrical Engineering from bygone years, 'What one fool can do, another can'. The principles are there, new sources of light are there, the expertise is there if used judiciously, and perhaps we can look to a new enlightened age for church lighting, which will accord with understanding of church architecture and the religious message contained in the church service, apart from giving substance to the WELCOME which the Church is anxious to encourage.

BIBLIOGRAPHY

Dr W Bordass: *Heating your Church*
Lighting and Wiring of Churches
both published by the Council for the Care of Churches
and available from:

> Church House Bookshop
> 31 Great Smith Street
> London SW1P 3BN

CIBS CODE – For Interior Lighting
Published by the Chartered Institution of Building Services Engineers
and available from:

> Delta House
> 222 Balham High Road
> London SW12 9BS

Publication lists relating to energy efficiency are available from:

> The Energy Efficiency Office
> Department of the Environment
> Blackhorse Road
> London SE8 5JH

> *or*

> Enquiries Bureau
> BRECSU
> Building Research Establishment
> Garston
> Watford WD2 7JR

> *or* your Regional Energy Efficiency Officer.